The Ten Wonders Of The Bible

By
Don Stewart

The Ten Wonders Of The Bible

By
Don Stewart

Dart Press
Orange, California 92613

The Ten Wonders Of The Bible
by Don Stewart

© Copyright 1990 by Don Stewart
Published by Dart Press
Box 6486
Orange, California 92613

ISBN 1-877825-03-4

PRINTED IN THE UNITED STATES OF AMERICA

Scripture quotations are used from The Holy Bible, New King James Bible, © 1979, 1980, 1982 by Thomas Nelson Inc. Nashville, Tennessee and are used by permission.

Table of Contents

Introduction

The Bible is the greatest book ever written. Inside its pages are the answers to the most important questions of life: "What is life all about?" "Who am I?" "Why am I here?" "Where am I going?"

The message of the Bible centers around the person of Jesus Christ—Lord of the universe and Savior of all creation.

The Bible has been recognized as a book in a class by itself. Consider the following testimonies to its character:

Victor Hugo: "England has two books, the Bible and Shakespeare. England made Shakespeare, but the Bible made England."

Abraham Lincoln: "I believe the Bible is the best gift God has ever given to man. All the good from the Saviour of the world is communicated to us through this book.

Andrew Jackson: "That book, sir, is the rock on which our republic stands."

Charles Dickens: "The New Testament is the very best book that ever was or ever will be known in the world."

Immanuel Kant: "The existence of the Bible, as a book for the people, is the greatest benefit which the human race has ever experienced. Every attempt to belittle it is a crime against humanity."

The Wonders of the Bible

As there were wonders of the ancient world there are also "wonders" of the Bible. These are characteristics that set the Bible apart from all other literature, ancient and modern. We will examine ten specific areas which make the Bible different from all other books.

Let us consider the *Ten Wonders of the Bible* . . .

Born in the East and clothed in Oriental form and imagery, the Bible walks the ways of all the world with familiar feet and enters land after land to find its own everywhere. It has learned to speak in hundreds of languages to the heart of man. Children listen to its stories with wonder and delight, and wise men at its warnings, but to the wounded and penitent it has a mother's voice. It has woven itself into our dearest dreams; so that Love, Friendship, Sympathy, Devotion, Memory, Hope, put on the beautiful garments of its treasured speech. No man is poor or desolate who has this treasure for his own. When the landscape darkens, and the trembling pilgrim comes to the Valley of the Shadow, he is not afraid to enter; he takes the rod and staff of Scripture in his hand; he says to friend and comrade, 'Goodbye; We shall Meet Again'; and confronted by that support, he goes toward the lonely pass as one who walks through darkness into light.

Henry Van Dyke

THE WONDER OF
THE BIBLE'S
INTELLIGENT FAITH

Jesus said, "You shall love the Lord your God with all
your heart with all your soul, and with all your mind"
(Matthew 22:37)

1
The Wonder Of The Bible's Intelligent Faith

One of the Bible's most wonderful features is the relevance it has for modern man. Although the Scriptures were composed between two and four thousand years ago, it still has the power to challenge intelligent men and women in the twentieth century. The Bible can stand the test of the most rigorous academic assault and will prove to be intellectually satisfying to anyone honestly investigating the evidence.

Intelligent faith

The Bible encourages people to put their faith in God. Unfortunately, many people equate faith with a blind leap in the dark or wishful thinking. But the faith that the Bible requires is intelligent faith. It is neither blind nor irrational. Biblical faith is a committing trust with an object (God) who is worthy of our faith. No one is asked to sacrifice his intellect when he puts his faith in the God of the Bible.

Christian faith is based upon the solid foundation of what God has done in history. He has revealed Himself to man and this revelation is recorded in the Scriptures. The Bible tells us what God requires of us and that we are to respond to Him by faith. In doing so, we are not expected to stop thinking or to act irrationally.

Jesus emphasized that coming to God involves the mind as well as the heart and soul: "You shall love the Lord your God with all your heart, with all your soul, and with all your mind" (Matthew 22:37).

When Jesus had a conversation with one of the scribes, He equated intelligence with knowing God: "So when Jesus saw that he answered wisely, He said to him, 'You are not far from the kingdom of God' " (Mark 12:34).

An intelligent response from the scribe caused Jesus to say that the man was close to the kingdom of God. This is another indication that the Bible encourages people to use their minds when examining the evidence.

The Apostle Paul told people to investigate the claims of Christianity to see if they were true: "Test all things; hold fast what is good" (1 Thessalonians 5:21).

The biblical writers encouraged people to investigate the Christian faith because they knew the events they recorded were true. Simon Peter showed that the New Testament writers were aware of the difference between mythology and fact: "For we did not follow cunningly devised fables when we made known to you the power and coming of our Lord Jesus Christ, but were eyewitnesses of His majesty" (2 Peter 1:16-17).

Since the New Testament writers were eyewitnesses to the events they recorded, they welcomed an honest investigation of the facts. Blind faith never was encouraged.

God does not expect us to act in faith toward Him unless that faith is an intelligent faith built upon the solid foundation of what He has done in history and what He has recorded in His Word.

Evidence is sufficient

The historical evidence that Christianity is true is more than sufficient. Historian E. M. Blaiklock writes, "I claim to be a historian. My approach to classics is historical. And I tell you that the evidence for the life, death, and the resurrection of Christ is better authenticated than most of the facts of ancient history, which I taught for forty-two years as a university teacher with some confidence. I said that Christ was quite different from anyone I had ever seen. And as a figure of history, Christ is precisely that. Four small books of simple Greek, called the Gospels, picture a person who was not the product of His times, but remote from human conception or expectation—so remote that His own men never fully understood Him, until an astounding event transformed them, enlightened them, and so launched them on the world that the dozen of them infiltrated the Roman Empire in a generation. Their successors beat the Empire to its knees in three centuries.

"Here are the alternatives. Either four men, only one of them with any education in the liberal sense of the word, invented the Character who altered the whole course of history, or they wrote of One they knew or had heard about from those who knew Him, a person so extraordinary that He could claim deity, sinlessness, all authority, and rouse no revulsion among those who long knew Him intimately . . . The religious leaders, collaborators with the occupying power, so feared Him that they betrayed and murdered Him, and in so doing . . . loosed forces which swept the world" (E. M. Blaiklock, ed. *Why I am Still a Christian,* Grand Rapids, MI: Zondervan Publishing House, 1971, p. 16).

There have been many cases of people who attempted to disprove the message of the Bible and have ended up becoming believers. In his book, *Man Alive,* author Michael Green provides two examples of such individuals:

At the turn of the century there was a man named Frank Morrison who, "had been brought up in a rationalistic environment, and had come to the opinion that the resurrection was nothing but a fairy tale happy ending that spoiled the matchless story of Jesus. Therefore, he planned to write an account of the last tragic days of Jesus, allowing the full horror of the crime and the full heroism of Jesus. He would, of course, omit any suspicion of the miraculous, and would utterly discount the resurrection. But when he came to study the facts with care, he had to change his mind, and he wrote his book on the other side. His first chapter is significantly called, 'The Book that Refused to Be Written,' and the rest of his volume consists of one of the shrewdest and most attractively written assessments I have ever read . . .

"Two able young men, Gilbert West and Lord Lyttleton, went up to Oxford . . . determined to attack the very basis of the Christian faith. So Lyttleton settled down to prove that Saul of Tarsus was never converted to Christianity, and West to demonstrate that Jesus never rose from the tomb.

"Some time later, they met to discuss their findings. Both were a little sheepish. For they had come independently to similar and disturbing conclusions. Lyttleton found, on examination, that

Saul of Tarsus did become a radically new man through his conversion to Christianity; and West found that the evidence pointed unmistakably to the fact that Jesus did rise from the dead. You may still find his book in a large library. It is entitled *Observations on the History and Evidences of the Resurrection of Jesus Christ*, and was published in 1747. On the fly-leaf he has had printed his telling quotation from Ecclesiasticus 11:7, which might be adopted with profit by any modern agnostic: 'Blame not before thou hast examined the truth' " (Michael Green, *Man Alive*, Downers Grove: Intervarsity Press, 1968, pp. 54-56).

Twentieth-century men and women can take the Bible, intelligently examine it, and find it satisfying. It truly is a wonder that this ancient book does meet the intellectual needs for modern man.

THE WONDER OF THE BIBLE'S HARMONY

Jesus said, "The Scripture cannot be broken"
(John 10:35)

2
The Wonder Of The Bible's Harmony

A characteristic that sets the Bible apart from other literature, both ancient and modern, is its harmony or unity. The Bible is a compilation of books written over a long period of time. However, it contains one unfolding story from beginning to end. The Bible is made up of 66 separate books, yet consistently it reveals one dynamic message—the dealings of a loving God with mankind through His Son, Jesus Christ.

Fifteen hundred years

The 39 books of the Old Testament and 27 of the New Testament were composed over a period of approximately 1,500 years. Probably the first books written were what we know as the books of Moses or the Law of Moses (Genesis, Exodus, Leviticus, Numbers, and Deuteronomy), composed around 1400 B.C. The last books of the New Testament were written around A.D. 90 and include the writings of the Apostle John (the Gospel of John, 1, 2, and 3 John, and Revelation). The composition of Genesis through Revelation, therefore, involves a time span of around 1,500 years.

Forty authors from different backgrounds

These 66 books were composed by over 40 different authors who came from a variety of educational and cultural backgrounds. For example, Joshua, was a military general; the prophet Daniel was a prime minister; David and Hosea were shepherds; Luke a doctor; Paul a Rabbi and tentmaker; Peter and John fishermen; and Nehemiah a court servant. The writers' backgrounds were remarkably diverse.

Different places

The books of the Bible were written in a variety of places on three different continents: Africa, Asia, and Europe. For example, the prophet Ezekiel wrote his work while held captive in Babylon. The Apostle Paul wrote four of his letters from prison in Rome. King David penned some of his psalms while he was a fugitive in the wilderness. Jeremiah was in the dungeon while he was composing his work. John, the beloved Apostle, wrote while a prisoner banished to the Isle of Patmos. The fact that these authors wrote from different geographical locales shows that God could and would reveal His word wherever He wished. It was not a situation, similar to other religions, where a person had to be in one particular place to receive the word from the gods or God. The God of the Bible has revealed Himself in a variety of different places.

Three languages

The books of the Bible were written in three different languages, Hebrew, Aramaic, and Greek. For the most part, the Old Testament was written in Hebrew (there are a handful of chapters in Daniel and Ezra composed in Aramaic). The New Testament was entirely written in the common Greek of the day, called *koine*.

Controversial subjects

From beginning to end, the Bible deals with a number of controversial subjects. These include: the origin of the universe, the existence and nature of God, the nature and purpose of mankind and the origin and extent of evil.

Chaos?

One would expect that the result of such diversity of authors, languages, backgrounds, and subjects to be chaos. Naturally we would expect the text to be full of contradictions and distortions. The wonder is that the Bible is completely consistent, harmonious and trustworthy. None of the authors or books is either internally or externally contradictory. The Bible's remarkable harmony in its continually unfolding story of redemption is a true wonder.

F.F. Bruce remarks, "The Bible, at first sight, appears to be a collection of literature—mainly Jewish. If we enquire into the circumstances under which the various Biblical documents were written, we find that they were written at intervals over a space of nearly 1400 years. The writers wrote in various lands, from Italy in the west to Mesopotamia and possibly Persia in the east. The writers themselves were . . . not only separated from each other by hundreds of years and hundreds of miles, but belonging to the most diverse walks of life. In their ranks we have kings, herdsmen, soldiers, legislators, fishermen, and a Gentile physician, not to speak of others of whom we know nothing apart from the writings they have left us. The writings themselves belong to a great variety of literary types. They include history, law (civil, criminal, ethical, ritual, sanitary), allegory, biography, personal correspondence, personal memoirs and diaries, in addition, to the distinctively Biblical types of prophecy and apocalyptic.

"For all that, the Bible is not simply an anthology; there is a unity which binds the whole together. An anthology is compiled by an anthologist, but no anthologist compiled the Bible" (F.F. Bruce, *The Books and the Parchment*, Rev. Ed., Westwood: Fleming Revell Co. 1963, p. 88).

Christ-Centered

The main theme of the Bible is the person of Jesus Christ. Both the Old and New Testaments testify to Jesus Christ as the Lord of Glory.

Jesus told the religious rulers of His day that the Old Testament Scriptures spoke of Him: "You search the Scriptures, for in them you think you have eternal life; and these are they which testify of Me . . . For if you believed Moses, you would believe Me; for he wrote about Me" (John 5:39,46). According to Jesus, Old Testament history is *His story.*

Old Testament—Preparation

The Old Testament prepares for the coming of the promised deliverer known as the Messiah. The prophet Isaiah spoke of, "The voice of one crying in the wilderness: prepare the way of the Lord; make straight in the desert a highway for our God" (Isaiah 40:3).

The theme that runs throughout the entire Old Testament is the establishment of the kingdom of God through the reign of the Messiah. The Old Testament looks forward to His coming.

Gospels—Manifestation

The gospels record the manifestation of the predicted Messiah. The New Testament testifies of the arrival of the one promised in the Old Testament: "In the beginning was the Word, and the Word was with God, and the Word was God . . . And the Word became flesh, and dwelt among us, and we beheld His glory, glory as of the only begotten from the Father, full of grace and truth . . . The next day John saw Jesus coming toward him, and said, 'Behold! the Lamb of God who takes away the sin of the world' " (John 1:1, 14, 29).

Jesus of Nazareth is the fulfillment of Old Testament prophecy regarding the promised Savior.

Acts—Propagation of Jesus' message

The Messiah Jesus came as predicted but was not accepted by His people. He died on a cross for the sins of the world and three days later rose from the dead. Forty days after His resurrection He ascended into heaven. Before returning to heaven, Jesus told His disciples: "But you shall receive power when the Holy Spirit has come upon you; and you shall be witnesses to Me in Jerusalem, and in all Judea and Samaria, and to the end of the earth" (Acts 1:8). They were instructed to tell others the gospel or good news of His death and resurrection. The propagation of the message of the risen Christ is recorded in the Book of Acts.

Paul—Explanation of Jesus' Coming

In his letters, the Apostle Paul, gives the explanation of the two comings of Christ: "To them God willed to make known what are the riches of the glory of this mystery among the Gentiles: which is Christ in you, the hope of glory" (Colossians 1:27).

The mystery or "sacred secret " that now has been revealed is that Christ came the first time to die and will come a second time to rule.

Revelation—Consummation of all things

Finally, we come to the Book of Revelation, which records Christ coming back to rule and reign upon the earth: "Behold He is coming with clouds, and every eye will see Him, and they also who pierced Him" (Revelation 1:7). All things that have been predicted in both the Old and New Testament will be consummated in the return of Jesus Christ.

The Old Testament records the preparation for the coming of Christ, the Gospels record His coming. The Book of Acts chronicles the propagation of the gospel (the good news) concerning Jesus Christ and the letters of Paul explain the implications of the gospel for our lives. The Book of Revelation describes the Second Coming of Jesus Christ and the establishment of His eternal kingdom.

The Bible glorifies Jesus Christ and centers on Him. It is one harmonious message from beginning to end.

A challenge

Those who do not consider the harmony of the Bible as something amazing, should accept the following challenge. Locate fifteen people who all speak the same language, have the same amount of education, and come from the same social background. Put them in separate rooms and ask them to write their opinion on only two controversial subjects, such as the nature and existence of God, and the purpose of life here on earth.

Would you expect their writings to agree? Would you find one unfolding account from beginning to end with no contradictions or distortions? Not at all. You would expect to get about fifteen different opinions.

Then how can we explain the unity of the Bible? The Bible consists of forty authors, not fifteen, writing from different educational backgrounds, different languages, and different cultures and on many different subjects. Yet, they write with complete unity and harmony.

One author

The explanation that the Bible gives for its remarkable unity is that it is inspired by God. The author of the books of the Bible is God the Holy Spirit. The Bible says, "All Scripture is given by inspiration of God, and is profitable for doctrine, for reproof, for correction, for instruction in righteousness" (2 Timothy 3:16). "Knowing this first, that no prophecy of Scripture is of any private interpretation, for prophecy never came by the will of man, but holy men of God spoke as they were moved by the Holy Spirit" (2 Peter 1:20-21).

Hence, the harmony of the Bible can be understood by realizing that the ultimate author behind the books is God. This fact puts the Bible in a class by itself.

It is evidence like this that led the great archaeologist, W. F. Albright, to conclude, "The Bible towers in content above all earlier religious literature; and it towers just as impressively over all subsequent literature in the direct simplicity of its message and . . . its appeal to men of all lands and times" (W.F. Albright, *The Christian Century*, November, 1958).

THE WONDER OF
THE BIBLE'S
SURVIVAL

Jesus said, "Heaven and earth will pass away but my
words will by no means pass away" (Matthew 24:35)

3
The Wonder Of The Bible's Survival

The next wonder that we will consider is the survival of the Bible. The fact that the complete text of Scripture has survived throughout history is a wonderful testimony to the preserving power of God.

Survived through time

The first book of the Bible was written some 3,500 years ago while the last was completed nearly 2000 years ago. The originals (autographs) of each biblical book were written on perishable surfaces and have long since disappeared. We are now dependent upon copies and copies of copies to reconstruct the text. The texts are reconstructed through the science of textual criticism. When textual criticism is applied to the books of the Bible we are assured that the text we have today is an accurate representation of the original. The text of the Bible not only has survived throughout the centuries, it has survived virtually unchanged.

Old Testament

From the time of their composition, the books of the Old Testament were considered holy by the Jews. They were not ordinary literature or history; they were God's Divine Word communicated to His people. Because these books were held in such high regard, the people took great care to preserve the texts precisely as they were originally written.

The Bible says the priests in Israel were responsible for the preservation of the Law. They were to store the sacred writings beside or in the Ark of the Covenant. The Ark was placed in the Holy of Holies in the Tabernacle while the Israelites were wandering in the wilderness. When the temple eventually was built in Jerusalem, the Ark was placed in the Holy of Holies in the Temple. The Old Testament records the command for the placement of the Law: "Take this Book of the Law, and put it beside the ark of the covenant of the Lord your God, that it may be there as a witness against you" (Deuteronomy 31:26).

The kings of Israel were required to have the Law as a guide in their administration: "Also it shall be, when he sits on the throne of his kingdom, that he shall write for himself a copy of this law in a book from the one before the priests, the Levites. And it shall be with him, and he shall read it all the days of his life, that he may learn to fear the Lord his God and be careful to observe all the words of this law and these statutes" (Deuteronomy 17:18,19).

Since these writings were considered holy, they were preserved with the greatest of care. The historical evidence reveals that this preservation was consistent and precise.

Fortunately, we have an unbroken historical tradition concerning the people responsible for the preservation of the text. The Mishnah (compiled in A.D 200) is a written record of the Jewish oral traditions from the time of Moses until the first century A.D. The Mishnah says, "Moses received the Law from Sinai and committed it to Joshua, and Joshua to the elders, and the elders to the Prophets, and the Prophets committed it to the men of the Great Synagogue. They said three things: be deliberate in judgment, gather up many disciples, and make a fence around the Law" (H. Danby. trans. *The Mishnah.* London: Oxford University Press, 1967, p. 446).

The Sopherim

The Mishnah informs us that from the completion of the Old Testament (400 B.C.), until A.D. 500, the transmission and care of the Old Testament text was in the hands of a group of scribes called the *Sopherim* ("counters"). The scribes were given this name because of the manner in which they checked the accuracy of the texts they were copying. These "counters" counted the number of letters in each completed copy and the number of words in each section of Scripture and compared them to the texts from which they copied.

As transmitters of God's sacred Word, the Sopherim went to great lengths to insure the purity of the text.

The Massoretes

Eventually a group of specialists arose to become the preservers of the body of Jewish tradition. This included the sacred writings, laws, history, and tradition of the people. These specialists were known as the Massoretes. Their name was derived from the Hebrew word *Massorah,* meaning "tradition." The Massoretes worked in both Palestine and Babylon from approximately A.D. 500 to A.D. 900. The Massoretes contributed to the textual preservation of the Old Testament in several significant ways.

First, the Massoretes collected all the textual-critical remarks of the rabbis, all the additional marks added to the margins of the sacred texts (which include memory devices, and pronunciation aids), and entered these in the side margins of the copies they made. They also did extensive tabulations concerning the contents of the text which were added to the upper and lower margins of the page.

These specialists considered the text so holy that they never altered it even when the text they were copying contained an obvious error. In such an instance, the procedure was to enter the error into the text they were producing and then enter remarks in the margin concerning how it could be corrected.

The contributions of the Massoretes to the preservation of the text of the Old Testament cannot be underestimated. They not only enhanced understanding of the text by their marginal contributions, they also carefully preserved all of the alternative or variant readings of the texts. This service has proved invaluable to today's textual critics in their work to determine the Old Testament's original text.

Biblical and literary scholar Sir Frederic Kenyon commented on the work of the Massoretes: "Besides recording varieties of reading, tradition, or conjecture, the Massoretes undertook a number of calculations which do not enter into the ordinary sphere of textual criticism. They numbered the verses, words, and letters of every book. They calculated the middle word and middle letter of each. They enumerated verses which contained all the letters of the alphabet, or a certain number of them; and so on. These trivialities, as we may rightly consider them, had yet the effect of securing minute attention to the precise transmission of the text; and they are but an excessive manifestation of a respect for the sacred Scriptures which in itself deserves nothing but praise. The Massoretes were indeed anxious that not one jot nor tittle, not one smallest letter nor tiny part of a letter of the Law should pass away or be lost" (Sir Frederic G. Kenyon, *Our Bible and Ancient Manuscripts.* New York: Harper and Row, Publishers, 1941, p. 38).

Dead Sea Scrolls

Though the work of the Massoretes assured us of the careful transmission of the text, the oldest surviving complete manuscript of the Old Testament dated from around A.D. 1000. This is a full 1,400 years after the completion of the Old Testament. Because of this long time span there were those who speculated that significant changes could have crept into the text.

This speculation ended in 1947. In that year a dramatic event occurred that revolutionized Old Testament textual criticism. A young Bedouin goat herder was searching for a lost goat in the caves in the cliffs above Wadi Qumran, located about a mile southwest of the northwest corner of the Dead Sea. In one of the caves he found several clay jars. These jars stood over two feet high and were approximately ten inches wide. In each of those jars he found leather scrolls wrapped in linen cloth. Shortly after his discovery, some of the scrolls fell into the hands of an antique dealer in Bethlehem while others were obtained by the archbishop of the Syrian Orthodox monastery in Jerusalem.

One of the first persons to examine the scrolls was the scholar E. L. Sukenik, of the Hebrew University of Jerusalem. Sukenik immediately recognized their antiquity and value and contacted other scholars for verification. The amazing find was confirmed by Dr. W. F. Albright, one of the world's leading archaeologists. Albright labeled the find "the most important Old Testament manuscript discovery ever made."

The recovery of the Qumran scrolls was halted by the Arab-Israeli war. It was not possible to go back to investigate further until the peace of 1948. The investigation then revealed hundreds of scrolls in a dozen different caves placed there by a Jewish sect called the Essenes. The Essenes had established a fortress nearby which they occupied from about 100 B.C. to around A.D. 68, when they fled the advancing Roman armies. Before they abandoned their community, they carefully hid their library in the nearby caves of Wadi Qumran, where they lay undisturbed for almost 1,900 years.

Analysis showed that most of the scrolls were written between 100 B.C. and A.D. 68. They contain portions of every book of the Old Testament (except Esther) as well as numerous documents relating to the doctrines and practices of the Essene community. One of the most significant finds was a complete copy of the book of Isaiah. The Isaiah scroll, found in Cave 1, dates one hundred years before Christ. In addition, an important fragment of Samuel, dating 400 years before the birth of Christ, was found in Cave 4. These, as well as other significant finds, revolutionized Old Testament textual criticism. The scrolls from Qumran were given the name "the Dead Sea Scrolls."

Shows accuracy of text

The Dead Sea Scrolls provide for us irrefutable evidence that the present Old Testament text has been faithfully copied from the originals. This is in spite of transmission through long centuries. Scholars Norman Geisler and William Nix provide us with an example of that faithfulness by comparing the contemporary Hebrew text of Isaiah 53 with the same chapter in the Isaiah scroll from the Dead Sea Scrolls:

"Of the 166 words in Isaiah 53, there are only seventeen letters in question. Ten of these letters are simply a matter of spelling, which does not affect the sense. Four more letters are minor stylistic changes, such as conjunctions. The remaining three letters comprise the word 'light,' which is added in verse 11, and does not affect the meaning greatly . . . Thus, in one chapter of 166 words, there is only one word (three letters) in question after a thousand years of transmission—and this word does not significantly change the meaning of the passage" (Norman Geisler and William Nix, *A General Introduction to the Bible.* Chicago, Moody Press, 1968, p. 26).

After comparing the entire Isaiah manuscript from the Dead Sea Scrolls with the present Hebrew text of Isaiah, Old Testament scholar Gleason L. Archer concluded that the Dead Sea Scrolls, "proved to be word for word identical with our standard Hebrew Bible in more that 95 percent of the text. The 5 percent of variation consisted chiefly of obvious slips of the pen and variations in spelling" (Gleason L. Archer, *A Survey of Old Testament Introduction.* Chicago, Moody Press, 1968, p. 263).

The discovery of the Dead Sea Scrolls laid to rest any speculation against the basic reliability of the Old Testament text.

Reverence for the text

Because the Jews considered the text so sacred, they refused to change it in any way. Editors and scribes, as we have observed, were reluctant to make changes even when it appeared obvious that the text from which they were copying had a copying error itself. Instead they would add a note referenced to the problem, while still preserving the error in the main body of the text. First-century Jewish historian Flavius Josephus recorded this reverence for the Scriptures: "We have given practical proof of our reverence of our own Scriptures. For, although such long ages have now passed, no one has ventured either to add, or to remove, or to alter a syllable; and it is an instinct with every Jew, from the day of his birth, to regard them as the decrees of God, to abide by them, and, if need be, cheerfully die for them. Time and time again ere now the sight has been witnessed of prisoners enduring tortures and death in every form in the theatres, rather than utter a single word against the laws and the allied documents" (Flavius Josephus, "Flavius Josephus Against Apion," in *Josephus' Complete Works.* Grand Rapids, MI: Kregel Publications, 1960, pp. 179, 180).

Summary and conclusion on Old Testament

As we have seen, the evidence in support of the trustworthiness of the Old Testament text is overwhelming.

Though the oldest parts of the Old Testament are probably 3,400 years old we can be confident that the text we possess today accurately represents what was originally written. We conclude this because of the following evidence:

1. Throughout the centuries the Jewish scribes viewed the text they were copying with reverence and care. They strongly believed they were copying God's Word.

2. When we compare the manuscripts from the Massoretic tradition among themselves there is very little variation in the text. Any variation that is found does not materially affect the meaning of the text.

3. The Dead Sea Scrolls provide overwhelming confirmation that the Hebrew texts were copied faithfully over a period of one thousand years.

Concerning the accuracy of the transmission of the Hebrew text, scholar Basil Atkinson, who was Under-Librarian of the library at Cambridge University, says it is "little short of miraculous."

William F. Albright, the dean of American archaeologists, concluded that, "We may rest assured that the consonantal text of the Hebrew Bible . . . has been preserved with an accuracy perhaps unparalleled in any other Near Eastern literature" (cited by H. H. Rowley, *Old Testament and Modern Study,* p. 25).

Hence when we read our present-day Old Testament we can have the assurance that we are reading the same thing that originally was written by the biblical writers.

New Testament

The books of the New Testament were originally written in the common Greek of the day called *koine.* In the first century, Greek was the international language. As is the case of the Old Testament, we do not possess the autographs (originals) of the New Testament books but are dependent on copies, and copies of copies to reconstruct the text. We will discover, as we did with the Old Testament, that we can have complete trust that the text of the New Testament has been transmitted to us in a reliable manner as well.

In the case of the New Testament there are three lines of evidence available to reconstruct the original: the Greek manuscripts, the versions (translations) and the writings of the church fathers.

Greek Manuscripts

The problem with almost all ancient writings is the lack of existing manuscripts to reconstruct the text. Most ancient writings have the slimmest manuscript evidence by which scholars attempt to establish the original.

In the case of the New Testament, however, there is no such problem because we are not lacking manuscripts to reconstruct the text. On the contrary, we have such an abundance of manuscripts that it makes the establishment of the text virtually certain.

In the history of the transmission of the Greek text there are different lines of evidence to reconstruct it: uncial manuscripts, minuscule manuscripts, lectionaries, and the papyri.

Uncial writing

Uncial writing consists of upper-case letters that are deliberately and carefully written. For example John 1:1 would look like this in uncial writing.

ΕΝΑΡΧΗΗΝΟΛΟΓΟΣΚΑΙΟΛΟΓΟΣΗΝΠΡΟΣΤΟΝΘΕΟΝΚΑΙΘΕΟΣΗΝ ΟΛΟΓΟΣ

Notice there is no punctuation in the sentence and no space between the words. Uncial manuscripts were written between the fourth and tenth centuries. In the ninth century A.D., uncial writing began to be replaced by a faster method known as minuscule writing.

Miniscules

Minuscule writing was a script of smaller letters not as carefully executed as uncials. By using minuscule writing, books could be turned out much faster. Minuscule writing was in use from the ninth to the sixteenth century.

Lectionaries

The third witness to the New Testament text are Scripture portions known as lectionaries. Textual scholar, Bruce Metzger, explains, "Lectionaries were the result of the Christian Church following the custom of the synagogue. Every Sabbath different portions of the Law and Prophets were read at services. Likewise the Christians developed a similar practice, reading a different portion of the Gospels and Epistles according to a fixed order of Sundays and Holy Days. These Scripture lessons are known as lectionaries" (Bruce Metzger, *The Text of the New Testament,* New York and Oxford: Oxford University Press, 1968, p. 263).

Fragments of lectionaries come from as early as the sixth century A.D., while complete manuscripts are found as early as the eighth century.

Papyri

The fourth line of evidence is the papyri. Papyrus is the material upon which the originals (autographs) of the New Testament were composed. Papyrus is an extremely perishable material, surviving only in warm, dry climates. The papyrus fragments that have survived, contain some of the earliest witnesses to the New Testament text. The surviving New Testament manuscripts written on papyrus employed the uncial script.

The surviving Greek manuscripts can be catalogued as follows:

Type of manuscript	Number surviving
Uncial	267
Minuscule	2,764
Lectionaries	2,143
Papyri	90
Total	5,264

Though the total number of surviving Greek manuscripts is larger than all other ancient works, they are not the only means available for reconstructing the original text.

Versions (Translations)

A second line of evidence by which the New Testament text can be established comes from the versions. Versions are translations of the different New Testament books into languages other than Greek. Ancient literature was rarely translated into another language with the New Testament being an important exception. From the very beginning, Christian missionaries, in an attempt to spread their faith, translated the New Testament into the various languages of the people they encountered. These translations, some made as early as the middle of the second century, give us an important witness to the text of that time.

When the copies of the manuscripts of the versions are catalogued, again we are faced with an overwhelming number (it should be noted that when we speak of manuscripts or copies we are referring to any part of a manuscript or copy that has survived. Thus the copy could be anything from a mere fragment to a complete text).

The following chart reveals the huge number of manuscripts of the early versions of the New Testament

Versions	Number of Manuscripts
Latin Vulgate	10,000 +(may be as high as 25,000)
Ethiopic	2,000 +
Slavic	4,101 +
Armenian	2,587 +
Syriac Peshitta	350 +
Bohairic	100 +
Total	19,000+

Because the versions are translations from the original Greek, they are not as valuable as the Greek manuscripts in reconstructing the text. However, they are an important witness to the text's reliability.

Comparisons to other ancient works

When the total manuscript evidence for the New Testament text (Greek manuscripts and early translations) is compared to other ancient writings the difference is striking.

Work	Date Written	Earliest Copy	Time Span	Number of Copies
Euripides	450 B.C.	A.D. 1100	1500 yrs.	9
Sophocles	450. B.C.	A.D. 1000	1400 yrs.	193
Catullus	54 B.C.	A.D. 1550	1550 yrs.	3
Homer	900 B.C.	400 B.C.	500 yrs.	643
N.T.	A.D. 40-100	A.D. 125	50 yrs.	24,000

When reconstructing the text of an ancient work, two key questions need to be considered. The first question deals with the time span between the date the work was completed and the earliest existing copy available to reconstruct the text. Usually, the shorter the time span the more dependable is the copy. The longer the time between the original and the copy, the more errors are apt to creep in as the text is copied and recopied.

As the above chart reveals, the time span between the composition of the New Testament and the earliest existing copy is much shorter than for the other ancient works. Using this standard of comparison, the New Testament is far superior in this regard.

The second question that needs to be addressed concerns the number of copies. "How many copies are available to reconstruct the text?" The more copies available, the better off we are—since there is more evidence to help one decide what the original text said.

For example, if an ancient work were to come down to us in only one copy, there would be nothing with which to compare that copy. There is no way of knowing if the scribe were incompetent since it could not be checked against another copy. J. Harold

Greenlee writes, "The probability that the original text of a document has been preserved is in part dependent upon two factors concerning the manuscripts. In the first place, the shorter the interval of time between the original documents and the date when the earliest available manuscript (or manuscripts) was written, the more likely it is that only a few copies intervene between this manuscript and the original. In the second place, the greater the number of available manuscripts, the greater is the probability that all of the original text has been preserved accurately among them" (J. Harold Greenlee, *Introduction to New Testament Textual Criticism,* Grand Rapids, MI: William B. Eerdmans Publishing Company, 1964, p. 13).

Comparing the New Testament with Homer's *Illiad* will illustrate the superiority of the evidence for Scripture. Textual scholar Bruce Metzger, former professor at Princeton University observes, "Of all the literary compositions by the Greek people, the Homeric poems are the best suited for comparison with the Bible . . . In the entire range of ancient Greek and Latin literature, the Illiad ranks next to the New Testament in possessing the greatest amount of manuscript testimony.

"In antiquity men [1] memorized Homer as later they were to memorize the Scriptures. [2] Each was held in the highest esteem and quoted in defense of arguments pertaining to heaven, earth, and Hades. [3] Homer and the Bible served as primers from which different generations of school boys were taught to read. [4] Around both there grew up a mass of scholia and commentaries. [5] They were both provided with glossaries. [6] Both fell into the hands of allegorists. [7] Both were imitated and supplemented—one with Homeric Hymns and writings such as the Batrachomyomachia, and the other with apocryphal books. [8] Homer was made available in prose analyses; the Gospel of John was turned into epic hexameters by Nonnus of Panopolis. [9] The manuscripts of both Homer and the Bible were illustrated. [10] Homeric scenes appeared in Pompeian murals; Christian basilicas were decorated with mosaics and frescoes of Biblical episodes" (Bruce Metzger, *Chapters in the History of New Testament Textual Criticism,* Grand Rapids, Eerdmans, 1963, pp. 144, 145).

When comparing the two, the New Testament overwhelms the *Illiad* in manuscript evidence. It must be remembered that, in sheer numbers of manuscripts, the *Iliad* is *second* to the New Testament of all the writings of antiquity.

The case for the reliability of the New Testament over other ancient writings is increased when further comparisons are made. New Testament expert, F. F. Bruce, explains, "Perhaps we can appreciate how wealthy the New Testament is in manuscript attestation if we compare the textual material for other ancient historical works. For Caesar's Gallic Wars (composed between 58 and 50 B.C.) there are several extant MSS, but only nine or ten are good, and the oldest is some 900 years later than Caesar's day. Of the 142 books of the Roman history of Livy (59 B.C.-A.D. 17), only 35 survive; these are known to us from not more than 20 MSS of any consequence, only one of which, and that containing fragments of Books III-VI, is as old as the fourth century. Of the 14 books of the Histories of Tacitus (ca. A.D. 100) only four and a half survive; of the 16 books of his Annals, 10 survive in full and two in part. The text of these extant portions of his two great historical works depend entirely on two MSS, one of the ninth century and one of the eleventh.

"The extant MSS of his minor works . . . all descend from a codex of the tenth century. The history of Thucydides (ca. 460-400 B.C.) is known to us from eight MSS, the earliest belonging to ca A.D. 900, and a few papyrus scraps, belonging to about the beginning of the Christian era. The same is true of the history of Herodotus (B.C. 488-428). Yet no classical scholar would listen to an argument that the authenticity of Herodotus or Thucydides is in doubt because the earliest MSS of their works which are of any use to us are over 1,300 years later than the originals" (F.F. Bruce, *The New Testament Documents: Are They Reliable?*, 5th Revised Edition. Downers Grove: Inter-Varsity Press, 1972, pp. 16, 17).

Bruce Metzger continues the same thought: "The works of several ancient authorities are preserved to us by the thinnest possible thread of transmission. For example, the compendious history of Rome by Velleius Paterculus survived to modern times in only one incomplete manuscript, from which the *editio princeps* was made—and this lone manuscript was lost in the seventeenth century after being copied . . . Even the Annals of the famous historian Tacitus is extant, so far as the six books are concerned, in but a single manuscript, dating from the ninth century. In 1870 the only known manuscript of the Epistle to Diognetus, an early Christian composition which editors usually included in the corpus of Apostolic Fathers, perished in a fire at the municipal library at Strasbourg. In contrast with these figures, the textual critic of the New Testament is embarrassed by the wealth of his material" (Bruce Metzger, *The Text of the New Testament.* New York and Oxford: Oxford University Press, 1968, p. 34).

With such a wealth of manuscript evidence we have every right to assume that nothing has been lost from the original New Testament text. Yet, the Greek manuscripts and the versions do not exhaust the lines of evidence.

The Church Fathers

A third line of evidence, used in establishing the New Testament text, are quotations from the writings of the early Christians known as the "church fathers." In their writings, they often quoted from the New Testament text. Every time we find a biblical quotation in their writings, we have a further witness to the text.

For example, seven letters have survived which were written by a man named Ignatius (A.D. 70-110). In those letters he quoted from 18 different books of the New Testament. Every time he cites Scripture, we can observe the Greek text he was using.

Thus, the early church fathers provide us with an excellent early witness to the text. We must be careful, however, in relying too heavily on the fathers because sometimes their quotations were paraphrases (not word for word) of the biblical text. In addition, the manuscripts of their writings have gone through a period of copying, during which mistakes have slipped into the documents. Nevertheless, their writings remain an important witness to the New Testament.

The number of quotations of the fathers is so overwhelming that, if every other source for the New Testament (Greek manuscripts, versions) were destroyed, the text could be reconstructed merely on the writings of the church fathers alone. In his book, *Our Bible—How We Got It,* Charles Leach relates the story of Sir David Dalrymple: "Sir David Dalrymple was wondering about the preponderance of Scripture in early writings when someone asked him. 'Suppose that the New Testament had been destroyed, and every copy of it lost by the end of the third century, could it have been collected again from the writings of the Fathers of the second and third centuries?' After a great deal of investigation Dalrymple concluded . . . 'You remember the question about the New Testament and the Fathers? That question roused my curiosity and as I possessed all the existing works of the Fathers of the second and third centuries, I commenced to search and up to this time I have found the entire New Testament, except eleven verses' " (Charles Leach, *Our Bible—How We Got It.* Chicago: Moody Press, 1898, pp. 35, 36).

Leo Vaganay remarked on the thorough research of scholar John Burgon: "Of the considerable volumes of unpublished material that Dean Burgon left when he died, of special note is his index of New Testament citations by the church Fathers of antiquity. It contains sixteen thick volumes to be found in the British Museum, and contains 86,489 quotations" (Leo Vaganay, *An Introduction to the Textual Criticism of the New Testament,* trans. by B.V. Miller, London: Sands and Co., 1937, p. 48).

Confidently we can say that when the evidence from the Greek manuscripts, the versions (translations) and the church fathers is considered, any impartial person cannot help but be impressed with their testimony.

At this point, the question of the variant readings usually arises.

Variant readings

When two manuscripts differ on a particular word or phrase in the text, the result is a variant reading. The difference may be of spelling, word order or different words used. The variations in the New Testament text arose both unintentionally and intentionally.

The greatest number of variants in the New Testament manuscripts are unintentional. They could creep into the text through faulty sight, hearing, writing, memory or judgment on the part of the scribe. Bruce Metzger declares, "In the earliest days of the Christian church after an apostolic letter was sent to a congregation or an individual, or after a gospel was written to meet the needs of a particular reading public, copies would be made in order to extend its influence and to enable others to profit from it as well. It was inevitable that such handwritten copies would contain a greater or lesser number of differences in wording from the original. Most of the divergencies arose from quite accidental causes, such as mistaking a letter or a word for another that looked like it. If two neighboring lines of a manuscript began or ended with the same group of letters or if two similar words stood next to each other in the same line, it was easy for the eye of the copyist to jump from the first group of letters to the second and so for a portion of the text to be omitted . . . Conversely the scribe might go back from the second to the first group and unwittingly copy one or more words (called dittography). Letters that were pronounced alike were sometimes confused . . . Such accidental errors were almost unavoidable whenever lengthy passages are copied by hand, and would be especially likely to occur if the scribe had defective eyesight, or was interrupted while copying, or, because of fatigue, was less attentive to his task than he should have been" (Bruce Metzger, *A Textual Commentary on the Greek New Testament.* London, New York, United Bible Societies, 1971, p. XV, XVI).

Intentional variation

Some of the variations came about intentionally as J. Harold Greenlee notes: "These comprise a significant, although a much less numerous, group of errors than the unintentional changes. They derive for the most part from attempts by scribes to improve the text in various ways. Few indeed are the evidences that heretical or destructive variants have been deliberately introduced into the mss" (J. Harold Greenlee, *New Testament Criticism,* p. 66).

Bruce Metzger expands upon the intentional variations: "Other divergencies in wording arose from deliberate attempts to smooth out grammatical or stylistic harshness, or to eliminate real or imagined obscurities of meaning in the text. Sometimes a copyist would add what seemed to him to be a more appropriate word or form, perhaps derived from a parallel passage . . . Thus during the years immediately following the composition of the several documents that eventually were collected to form the New Testament, hundreds if not thousands of variant readings arose" (Bruce Metzger, *Textual Commentary*, p. XVI.).

It is often assumed that the variant readings in the manuscripts undermine the reliability of the text. Some people point to 200,000 variants in the existing manuscripts and contend it is impossible to recover the New Testament's exact text and message. However, the facts say otherwise.

We have shown that some 25,000 manuscripts of the New Testament exist in Greek or one of the many versions. Every time a word or letter is different in a manuscript it is counted as a variant. For example, if a word is misspelled in 1,000 manuscripts it is counted as 1,000 variants. Most of the variants are of this variety and are only incidental to the meaning of the text. Consider the following:

In Matthew 17:10 some manuscripts read "the disciples" while others read "His disciples." Every time this difference occurs it is counted as a variant reading.

In Mark 7:24 some manuscripts read "Tyre and Sidon." Others read "Tyre." Every time they differ it is counted as a variant.

In John 19:7 some manuscripts read "our law." Others read "the law." Again, every time they differ it is counted as a variant reading.

Doesn't affect Christian doctrine

Since the variants do not greatly affect the meaning of the text, Christian doctrine is not affected. The introduction to the Revised Standard Version of the Bible says, "It will be obvious to the careful reader that still in 1946 as in 1881 and 1901, no doctrine of the Christian faith has been affected by the revision, for the simple reason that, out of the thousands of variant readings in the manuscripts, none has turned up thus far that requires a revision of Christian doctrine" (F.C. Grant, "An Introduction to the Revised Standard Version of the New Testament," *The New Testament, Revised Standard Version*, Nashville: Thomas Nelson, 1946, p. 42).

Scholar B. B. Warfield said that the New Testament "has been transmitted to us with no, or next to no, variation; and even in the most corrupt form in which it has ever appeared, to use the oft-quoted words of Richard Bentley, 'The real text of the sacred writers is competently exact' " (Benjamin B. Warfield, *Introduction to the Textual Criticism of the New Testament*, seventh edition. London: Hodder and Stoughton, 1907, p. 14).

Since we possess so many manuscripts, we can be assured the original text has been preserved. We never have to revert to guessing to determine what the text originally said. The great scholar Samuel Tregelles echoed this thought: "We possess so many mss, and we are aided by so many versions, that we are never left to the need to conjecture as the means of removing errata" (Samuel Tregelles, *Greek New Testament*, Prolegomena).

We can rightly conclude that the variations in the different manuscripts have no affect whatsoever on the reliability of the text or upon Christian theology.

Summary and conclusion on the New Testament

Although we do not possess the originals of any of the books of the New Testament, the evidence shows that it has been transmitted accurately throughout history. We summarize the evidence as follows:

1. The time span between the date of composition of the books of the New Testament and the earliest surviving manuscripts is relatively short. Most other ancient works have a much longer gap between the time when they were written and the earliest available manuscript. There is in existence a complete New Testament manuscript (Codex Vaticanus) which was copied within 250 years of the time of the writing of the New Testament. In addition, we have over fifty fragments of the New Testament that go back even earlier. The classical writings (Plato, Aristotle, etc.) are viewed as having been transcribed in a reliable manner, yet, the time span, between the original and

their earliest copy, is over a thousand years. The New Testament documents, if considered on the same basis, also must be considered trustworthy.

2 Not only is the interval shorter between the writings of the New Testament and the earliest existing manuscripts, the number of manuscripts (over 5,000 in Greek) is far superior to any other ancient work. Given the axiom, "The more manuscripts, the better chance to reconstruct the original," we again see that the New Testament is in much better shape than other ancient works.

3 The New Testament was translated into other languages at an early date. Those versions provide further evidence in establishing the true text. The number of manuscript copies of the different versions is around 20,000. Most other ancient writings were never translated into another language.

4 A further line of evidence is found in the writings of the church fathers, where verses, passages and entire books are cited. If the other sources for the New Testament were non-existent (Greek manuscripts and versions) the text still could be reconstructed through the writings of the church fathers. There is nothing like this for any other ancient work.

Given the above facts, we conclude that the New Testament has been accurately transcribed throughout history. Any contrary conclusion is based either on a willful desire not to accept the evidence as it stands, or ignorance of the facts.

Sir Frederic Kenyon, former keeper of ancient manuscripts and director of the British Museum, was an authority second to none on manuscript evidence. After a lifetime of study of ancient documents he came to the following conclusions: "It cannot be too strongly asserted that in substance the text of the Bible is certain . . . The number of manuscripts of the New Testament, of early translations from it, and of quotations from it in the oldest writers of the church, is so large that it is practically certain that the true reading of every doubtful passage is preserved in some one or other of these ancient authorities. This can be said of no other ancient book in the world" (Sir Frederic Kenyon, *Our*

Bible and Ancient Manuscripts, New York: Harper and Row Publishers, 1941, p. 23).

Kenyon also emphasized that, "The interval between the dates of the original composition and the earliest extant evidence becomes so small as to be in fact negligible, and the last foundation for any doubt that the Scriptures have come down to us substantially as they were written has now been removed. Both the authenticity and the general integrity of the books of the New Testament may be regarded as finally established" (Sir Frederic Kenyon, *The Bible and Archaeology*, New York: Harper and Row Publishers, 1940, p. 288).

Survived unrelenting persecution

What makes the survival of the text of Scripture even more remarkable is the persecution and criticism it has received. From the time the Bible was completed, it has been persecuted with an unrelenting fervor. No other book in history has received the same type of attacks as has the Bible.

The persecution of Diocletian is but one example of the type of persecution the Scriptures have endured. In A.D. 303, the Roman emperor Diocletian wrote an imperial letter ordering (1) the destruction of all Christian churches, (2) the burning of all Christian Scriptures, and (3) the loss of civil liberties by all professing Christians. Diocletian's edict did not stop the spread of Christianity or the production of copies of the Bible.

The historical irony is that Constantine, the Roman emperor who succeeded Diocletian, converted to Christianity and eventually ordered 50 copies of the Scriptures to be produced by the best scribes at government expense.

Survived criticism

The Scriptures have also survived criticism. No other book has been subjected to such thorough criticism as has been leveled at the Bible, yet the Bible has been equal to that challenge, withstanding the most rigorous criticism imaginable. Bernard Ramm observes that, "A thousand times over, the death knell of the Bible has been sounded, the funeral procession formed, the inscription cut on the tombstone, and committal read. But somehow the corpse never stays put. No other book has been so chopped, knived, sifted, scrutinized, and vilified. What book on philosophy or religion or psychology . . . of classical or modern times has been subject to such a mass attack as the Bible? With such venom and skepticism? With such thoroughness and erudition? Upon every chapter, line, and tenet?

"The Bible is still loved by millions, read by millions, and studied by millions" (Bernard Ramm, *Protestant Christian Evidences*, Chicago: Moody Press, 1957, pp. 232-233).

Impact of persecution and criticism

The impact of two thousand years of persecution and criticism of Scripture has been aptly summed up by H.L. Hastings: "Infidels for eighteen hundred years have been refuting and overthrowing this book, and yet it stands today as solid as a rock. Its circulation increases, and it is more loved and cherished and read today than ever before. Infidels with all their assaults, make about as much impression on this book as a man with a tack hammer would on the Pyramids of Egypt. When the French monarch proposed the persecution of the Christians in his dominion, and old statesmen and warrior said to him, 'Sire, the Church of God is an anvil that has worn out many hammers.' So the hammers of infidels have been pecking away at this book for ages, but the hammers are worn out, and the anvil still endures. If this book had not been the book of God, men would have destroyed it long ago. Emperors and popes, kings and priests, princes and rulers have all tried their hand at it; they die and the book still lives" (H.L. Hastings, as quoted by John Lea, *The Greatest Book in the World*. Philadelphia, PA: n.p., 1922, pp. 17, 18).

Though time passes, the Bible remains a dramatic testimony to the keeping power of God. Rulers and critics come and go but the Bible remains. The prophet Isaiah, speaking 2,700 years ago, declared, "The grass withers, the flowers fades, but the word of our God stands forever" (Isaiah 40:8).

The fact that the Scriptures have survived time, unrelenting persecution and criticism is a true wonder.

THE WONDER OF THE BIBLE'S HISTORICAL PRECISION

"Your Word is truth" (John 17:17)

4
The Wonder Of The Bible's Historical Precision

A feature that separates the Bible from all other ancient literature is its historical precision. Within the pages of the Bible we find many references to events, people and places. The science of archaeology, along with the testimony of secular historical records, confirm the precision of the references in the various biblical books. This minute attention to detail observed by the biblical writers is unparalleled in any other ancient literature. The late Jewish archaeologist Nelson Glueck declared, "It may be stated categorically that no archaeological discovery has ever controverted a biblical reference . . . [I assert] the almost incredible accurate historical memory of the Bible, and particularly so when it is fortified by archaeological fact" (Nelson Glueck, *Rivers in The Desert: History of Negev,* Philadelphia, PA: Jewish Publication Society of America, 1969, p. 84).

Importance

The question of whether the Bible is historically precise in its description of persons, places, and events is of crucial importance. The revelation of God to man was accomplished through His mighty words and deeds in history.

The Bible is a testimony of the mighty works of God: The Lord reminded His people of this: "I am the Lord your God, who brought you out of the land of Egypt, out of the house of bondage" (Exodus 20:2).

The nation was continually urged to remember these deeds of God. The Bible says, "But the Lord, who brought you up from the land of Egypt with great power and an outstretched arm . . . Him you shall worship" (2 Kings 17:36). "O My people, remember now . . . that you may know the righteousness of the Lord" (Micah 6:5).

Jesus Christ came into our world. The key verse of the New Testament says, "And the Word became flesh and dwelt among us, and we beheld His glory, the glory as of the only begotten of the Father, full of grace and truth" (John 1:14).

We see the writers of Scripture appealing time and time again to actual historical events to testify to the power and existence of God. The entire Bible centers around what God did in history.

Biblical scholar F. F. Bruce echoes these thoughts: "That Christianity has its roots in history is emphasized in the Church's earliest creeds, which fix the supreme revelation of God at a particular point in time, when 'Jesus Christ, His only Son our Lord . . . suffered under Pontius Pilate.' This historical 'once-for-all-ness' of Christianity, which distinguishes it from those religions and philosophical systems which are not specially related to any particular time, makes the reliability of the writings which purport to record this revelation a question of first-rate importance" (F.F. Bruce, *The New Testament Documents: Are They Reliable?* Downers Grove Il: Inter-Varsity Press, 1960, p. 8).

The need for historical precision

Some people say that the message is what is important, not whether the Bible is historically precise. Such is not the case, as attorney/theologian John Warwick Montgomery observes, "Christianity's claim to truth consists merely of a finger pointing back through time to an historical figure who divided world history into two parts—to Jesus of Nazareth—to His statements concerning Himself and true religion, and to the life He led attesting to the statements He made. An honest, historically accurate, scientific investigation of these data (involving chiefly a study of the documents collected in the New Testament) will show that Jesus claimed to be God Incarnate, that He described the only true (but not the only possible) religion consisting of fellowship with Himself, and that He attested His claims by a sinless life which profoundly affected everyone who crossed His path, and by a resurrection which left no doubt in the minds of eyewitnesses that He was in fact the true God" (John Warwick Montgomery, *The Shape of The Past: An Introduction to Philosophical Historiography*, vol. 1, Ann Arbor, Mich., Edwards Brothers, 1962, p. 328).

The historical accuracy of Scripture is of vital importance, for it is the appeal made by the Bible itself to argue for its truthfulness.

As we examine the evidence we will discover that the Scriptures are historically precise and that we have every reason to trust what they say.

Old Testament History

The Old Testament records events that span thousands of years. Biblical scholar John Bright correctly points out the Bible's own high view of history:

"The genius of the Old Testament faith does not lie in its idea of God or in the elevation of its ethical teachings. Rather it lies in its understanding of history, specifically of Israel's history, as the theatre of God's purposive activity. A concern with the meaning of history, and of specific events within history, is one of its most characteristic features. It records a real history, and it interprets every detail of that history in the light of Yahweh's sovereign purpose and righteous will. It relates past events—the stories of the Patriarchs, the Exodus, the giving of the Promised Land—in terms of his gracious dealings with his people, his promise to them and fulfillment. It continually sets forth the response that Yahweh requires of his people, and interprets their fortunes in the midst of events, in terms of their obedience or disobedience to his demands. And it announces that Yahweh will yet do, in the judgment of Exile and beyond, for the accomplishment of his purpose. The Old Testament consistently views Israel's history as one that is guided as a destination by the word and will of her God" (John Bright, *The Authority of the Old Testament*. London: SCM Press, 1967, p. 130).

R. K. Harrison, Old Testament scholar and historian, emphasized the important role of archaeology in confirming the historical accuracy of the Old Testament: "Archeology must not be regarded as the sole determining consideration in matters of historical criticism, since it, too, is beset with its own kind of problems. These include poor excavating techniques in earlier days, the varied interpretation of specific artifacts, and the difficulty of establishing an assured chronological framework into which events can be placed with confidence. Archaeology is in no sense an adequate 'control' mechanism by which OT sequences stand or fall.

"Nevertheless, archaeological discoveries have assisted enormously in demonstrating the historicity of certain OT events and personages, and in other areas have furnished an authentic social and cultural background against which many OT narratives can be set with assurance. Numerous cuneiform texts that have been unearthed show how the Mesopotamian writers of early historiographic material expressed themselves in terms of a world view, as is the case of the first few chapters of Genesis, thereby indicating that the latter should not be taken as myth, but as Mesopotamian historiography" (R. K. Harrison, Bruce Waltke, Donald Guthrie, and Gordon Fee, *Biblical Criticism: Historical, Literary and Textual*. Grand Rapids, MI: Zondervan Publishing House, 1978, pp. 6, 7).

Some Reversals In Old Testament Criticism

Not only has the basic history of the Old Testament period been confirmed by archaeological testimony, there also have been some startling reversals of Old Testament criticism.

Until this century, it was believed that Moses could not have written the first five books of the Old Testament because writing was said to be virtually unknown or, at least, not commonly used at his time. Representative of this thought was liberal scholar Herman Schultz, who wrote in 1898, "Of the legendary character of the pre-Mosaic narrators, the time of which they treat is a sufficient proof. It was a time prior to all knowledge of writing, a time separated by an interval of more than four hundred years, of which there is absolutely no history, from the nearest period of which Israel has some dim historical recollection, a time when in civilized countries writing was only beginning to be used for the most important matters of State. Now wandering herdsmen have invariably an instinctive dislike to writing. In fact, at the present day, it is considered a disgrace among Bedouin tribes in the peninsula of Sinai to be able to write. It is therefore impossible that such men could hand down their family histories, in themselves quite unimportant, in any other way than orally, to wit, in legends. And even when writing had come into use, in the time that is, between Moses and David, it would still be sparingly used, and much that happened to the people must still have been handed down simply as legend" (Herman Schultz, *Old Testament Theology*. H.A. Patterson, trans. Edinburgh: T&T Clark, 1898, pp. 88-90).

Note the use of terms such as "impossible" and "legend." The belief was that Moses could not have written the first five books of the Old Testament because of the lack of widespread use of writing and of his lack of interest in recording Israel's history.

Modern archaeological discoveries, however, show that writing was in common use prior to the time of Moses, and that Moses had the capacity to write the first five books of the Old Testament. D. J. Wiseman observes, "Well before the end of the second millennium the pressures of trade and need for communication led to the widespread use of their simple form of writing (e.g. in marking personal objects; cf. stone inscriptions of Ahiram). Thus, by the time of the entry of the Hebrews into Canaan in the Late Bronze Age they would be confronted, if not already familiar with at least five different forms of writing systems used for eight or more languages" (D.J. Wiseman and Edwin Yamauchi, *Archaeology and the Bible*. Grand Rapids, MI: Zondervan Publishing House, p. 25).

This is echoed by noted scholar Cyrus Gordon: "The excavations at Ugarit have revealed a high material culture in Canaan prior to the emergence of the Hebrews. Prose and poetry were already fully developed. The educational system was so advanced that dictionaries in four languages were compiled for the use of scribes, and the individual words were listed in their Ugaritic, Babylonian, Sumerian, and Hurrian equivalents. The beginnings of Israel are rooted in a highly cultural Canaan where the contributions of several talented peoples . . . have converged and blended. The notion that early Israelite religion and society were primitive is completely false. Canaan in the days of the Patriarchs was a hub of great international culture" (Cyrus Gordon, "Higher Critics and Forbidden Fruit," *Christianity Today*, November 23, 1959).

The Hittites

An ancient people, known as the Hittites, are mentioned some fifty times in the Old Testament. For a long time they were considered to be fabricated by the Bible because the only evidence of their existence came from the Old Testament. Liberal scholars assumed the biblical references to the Hittites were historically worthless. John Elder comments on modern confirmation of the Hittites: "One of the striking confirmations of Bible history to come from the science of archaeology is the 'recovery' of the Hittite peoples and their empires. Here is a people whose name appears again and again in the Old Testament, but who in secular history had been completely forgotten and whose very existence was considered to be extremely doubtful . . . But until the investigation of modern archaeologists, the Hittites remained a shadowy and undefined people" (John Elder, *Prophets, Idols, and Diggers,* New York: Bobbs-Merrill Company, 1960, p. 75).

Archaeologist A. H. Sayce was the first scholar to identify the Hittite people from a non-biblical source. In 1876 he released his information from the monuments and revolutionized critical theories concerning the Hittites.

In the twentieth century, much more information about the Hittites has come to light confirming the historical accuracy of the Old Testament. Fred H. Wight concludes, "Now the Bible picture of this people fits in perfectly with what we know of the Hittite nation from the monuments. As an empire they never conquered the land of Canaan itself, although Hittite local tribes did settle there at an early date. Nothing discovered by the excavators has in any way discredited the Biblical account. Scripture accuracy has once more been proved by the archaeologists" (Fred H. Wight, *Highlights of Archaeology in Bible Lands.* Chicago: Moody Press, 1955, pp. 94, 95).

Jesus' view

Another testimony of the trustworthiness of the Old Testament comes from Jesus Christ. When we examine the way Jesus viewed Scripture we can see that He trusted it totally. He said the Word of God was true: "Sanctify them by Your truth. Your word is truth" (John 17:17). Jesus also said the Scripture could not be broken (John 10:35).

It is clear from Jesus' statements that He believed the Bible to be historically accurate and without error. Old Testament authority John Bright summarizes Jesus' attitude toward Scripture: "I am quite unable to get around the fact . . . that the Old Testament was authoritative Scripture for Jesus himself. Jesus knew no Scripture save the Old Testament, no God save its God; it was this God whom He addressed as Father . . . never once did He suggest that in the light of His work they might safely be discarded. On the contrary, He regarded the Scriptures as the key to the understanding of His person; again and again He is represented as saying that it is the Scriptures that witness to Him and are fulfilled in Him. At no place did He express Himself as shocked by the Old Testament . . . Although the Old Testament on occasion offends our Christians feelings, it did not apparently offend Christ's Christian feelings! Could it really be that we are ethically and religiously more sensitive than He? Or is it perhaps that we do not view the Old Testament—and its God—as He did? The very fact that the Old Testament was normative Scripture to Jesus, from which He understood both His God and . . . Himself, means that it must in some ways be normative Scripture for us too—unless we wish to understand Jesus in some other way than He Himself did and the New Testament did" (John Bright, ibid. p. 77).

Summary

After briefly examining some of the historical and archaeological evidence in favor of the historical reliability of the Old Testament, we summarize with several observations:

1. The persons, places and events listed during the different periods of Old Testament history match up well with the facts and evidence from history and archaeology.

2. New evidence from recent discoveries has shown that certain Old Testament passages, once considered historically unreliable, are now found to be historically precise.

3. Above all, the Christian Church believes the Old Testament is historically reliable because of the testimony of Jesus Christ. Jesus claimed to be God in human flesh. These claims were later validated by His resurrection from the dead. Jesus taught that the Old Testament was the Word of God, totally accurate in all that it said. There can be no stronger confirmation than the testimony of Jesus.

Conclusion on the Old Testament

The archaeologist, John Elder, offers a fitting conclusion to the issue of the Old Testament's historical reliability: "It is not too much to say that it was the rise of the science of archeology that broke the deadlock between historians and the orthodox Christian. Little by little, one city after another, one civilization after another, one culture after another, whose memories were enshrined only in the Bible, were restored to their proper places in ancient history by the studies of archeologists . . . The over-all result is indisputable. Forgotten cities have been found, the handiwork of vanished peoples has reappeared, contemporary records of Biblical events have been unearthed and the uniqueness of biblical revelation has been emphasized by contrast and comparison to the newly understood religions of ancient peoples. Nowhere has archeological discovery refuted the Bible as history" (John Elder, *Prophets, Idols, and Diggers,* Bobbs-Merrill, Co. p. 18).

We conclude, there is every reason to believe the Old Testament is historically accurate.

New Testament History

The New Testament is primarily a record of the salvation work of Jesus Christ, the Son of God. Yet when the New Testament addresses historical issues, it too is accurate and reliable.

In the nineteenth century it was widely believed that the New Testament was an invention of the second-century church. Sir William Ramsay provides us with an example of how an honest scholar of history can change his perspective when faced by incontrovertible evidence from history and archaeology. Ramsay began his historical research toward the end of the nineteenth century when he was taught that the New Testament was not written in the first century and was not historically reliable. Although the New Testament Book of Acts contained a variety of eyewitness historical references, liberal critics rejected its historicity and declared it untrue.

As a young historian, Ramsay was determined to develop an independent historical/geographical study of first-century Asia Minor. He assumed the Book of Acts was unreliable and ignored its historical allusions in his studies. The amount of usable historical information concerning first-century Asia Minor, however, was too little for him to proceed very far with his work. That led him, almost in desperation, to consult the Book of Acts for any help possible. Ramsay discovered that it was remarkably accurate and true to first-century history and topography.

Ramsay testified to what changed his mind: "I may fairly claim to have entered on this investigation without prejudice in favour of the conclusions which I shall now seek to justify to the reader. On the contrary, I began with a mind unfavourable to it, for the ingenuity and apparent completeness of the Tübingen theory had at one time quite convinced me. It did not then lie in my line of life to investigate the subject minutely, but more recently I found myself brought into contact with the Book of Acts as an authority for the topography, antiquities and society of Asia Minor. It was gradually borne upon me that in various details the narrative showed marvelous truth. In fact, beginning with a fixed idea that the work was essentially a second century composition, and never relying on its evidence as trustworthy for first century conditions, I gradually came to find it a useful ally in some obscure and difficult investigations" (Sir William Ramsay, *St. Paul The Traveler and Roman Citizen*. Grand Rapids, MI: Baker Book House, 1962, p. 36).

Ramsay's study led him to conclude that "Luke's history is unsurpassed in respect to its trustworthiness" (Ramsay, ibid. p. 81) and "Luke is a historian of the first rank; not merely are his statements trustworthy . . . this author should be placed along with the very greatest of historians" (Sir William Ramsay, *The Bearing of Recent Discoveries on the Trustworthiness of the New Testament*. Grand Rapids, MI: Baker Book House, 1953, p. 222).

From the evidence gathered by Ramsay, we discover that Luke, author of the greatest portion of the New Testament (Luke and Acts) and an eyewitness of many events during the growth of the first-century church, was a careful historian.

Since many historical details, national boundaries, and government structures in Asia Minor were different in the second century from what they had been in the first, it is reasonable to conclude that the actual author of Luke and Acts was a first-century author, not a second-century one.

Acts 14:1-6, for example, was in historical dispute for many years. The passage implies that Lystra and Derbe were cities in the district of Lycaonia but Iconium was in a different district. Later Roman writers such as Cicero contradicted the passage, asserting that Iconium was also in Lycaonia. For years this was used to show the historical unreliability of Acts.

In 1910, however, Sir William Ramsay discovered an inscription declaring that the first century Iconium was under the authority of Phrygia from A.D. 37 to A.D. 72. It was only during these years that Iconium was not under the authority of Lycaonia. Not only did this discovery confirm the accuracy of the statement in Acts 14, it showed that whoever wrote this passage knew what district Iconium was in at that time. That places the author as an eyewitness to the events.

K. A. Kitchen gives further comment on Ramsay's work: "Ever since the . . . explorations and discoveries of William Ramsay earlier this century, the accuracy of Luke as a historian and reporter has been upheld by a multiplicity of details, particularly in the Book of Acts. He assigns the right titles to the proper officials at the correct periods of time in question. Such as the proconsul in Cyprus (Acts 13:7) and of Achaia (Acts 18:12), the Asiarchs at Ephesus (Acts 19:31), among others . . . Luke was careful to entitle Herod Antipas the *Tetrarch* of Galilee, not loosely 'king' as many of his subjects flatteringly did" (Kenneth Kitchen, *The Bible in Its World: The Bible and Archaeology Today*, Downers Grove IL: Inter-Varsity Press, 1977, pp. 132, 133).

The classical historian, A. N. Sherwin-White, declares, "For Acts the confirmation of historicity is overwhelming . . . any attempt to reject its basic historicity even in matters of detail must now appear absurd. Roman historians have long taken it for granted" (A. N. Sherwin-White, *Roman Society and Roman Law in the New Testament,* Oxford: At the Claredon Press, 1963, p. 189).

F. F. Bruce, a classical scholar turned biblical scholar, observes, "It is a curious fact that historians have often been much readier to trust the New Testament than have many theologians. Somehow or other, there are people who regard a 'sacred book' as *ipso facto* under suspicion, and demand much more corroborative evidence for such a work than they would for an ordinary secular or pagan writing. From the viewpoint of the historian, the same standards must apply to both" (F. F. Bruce, *The New Testament Documents: Are They Reliable?,* 5th rev. ed. Grand Rapids, Mich.: Wm. B. Eerdmans Publishing Co., 1984, p. 15).

New Testament Books: Primary source testimony

As we investigate the New Testament text we observe that the writers of the New Testament books claimed to be either eyewitnesses to the events recorded or those who gathered eyewitness testimony.

The Apostle John wrote, "That which was from the beginning, which we have heard, which we have seen with our eyes, which we have looked upon, and our hands have handled, concerning the Word of life—the life was manifested, and we have seen, and bear witness, and declare to you that eternal life which was with the Father and was manifested to us" (1 John 1:1-2).

Luke, the writer of the third gospel, penned these words: "Inasmuch as many have taken in hand to set in order a narrative of those things which are most surely believed among us, just as those who from the beginning were eyewitnesses and ministers of the word delivered them to us, it seemed good to me also, having had perfect understanding of all things from the very first, to write to you an orderly account, most excellent Theophilus, that you may know the certainty of those things in which you were instructed" (Luke 1:1-4).

This statement of Luke tells us, at least, the following:

1. Luke was not an eyewitness to the events he recorded.
2. But he, like those before him, made careful use of eyewitness accounts.
3. Luke had access to other narratives, written documents like his own.
4. Luke felt the need for a further account.
5. His account is orderly.
6. His ultimate aim is truth.

The fact that the New Testament writers claimed such objective, complete, and firsthand evidence concerning Jesus Christ is of the utmost importance. Their evidence is not hearsay or imaginary: it is direct and reliable as Biblical scholar F. F. Bruce observes, "The earliest preachers of the gospel knew the value of . . . first-hand testimony, and appealed to it time and time again. 'We are witnesses of these things,' was their constant and confident assertion. And it can have been by no means so easy as some writers seem to think to invent words and deeds of Jesus in those early years, when so many of His disciples were about, who could remember what had and had not happened.

"And it was not only friendly eyewitnesses that the early preachers had to reckon with; there were others . . . who were also conversant with the main facts of the ministry and death of Jesus. The disciples could not afford to risk inaccuracies (not to speak of willful manipulation of the facts), which would at once be exposed by those who would be only too glad to do so. On the contrary, one of the strong points in the original apostolic preaching is the confident appeal to the knowledge of the hearers; they not only said, 'We are witnesses of these things,' but also, 'As you yourselves know' (Acts 2:22). Had there been any tendency to depart from the facts in any material respect, the possible presence of hostile witnesses in the audience would have served as a further corrective" (F. F. Bruce, *The New Testament Documents: Are They Reliable?*, Downers Grove, IL: InterVarsity Press, 1964, pp. 33, 44-46).

Dating of the New Testament

When all the historical and textual evidence is amassed, it becomes clear that the New Testament was composed at a very early date by eyewitnesses or those who recorded eyewitness testimony. The eminent archaeologist William F. Albright concluded, "In my opinion, every book of the New Testament was written by a baptized Jew between the forties and the eighties of the first century A.D. (very probably sometime between A.D. 50 and 75)" (Interview with *Christianity Today*, January 18, 1963).

Albright also stated, "Thanks to the Qumran discoveries, the New Testament proves to be what it was formerly believed to be: the teaching of Christ and his immediate followers between cir. 24 and cir. 80 A.D." (W.F. Albright, *From Stone Age to Christianity*, Baltimore, MD: Johns Hopkins Press, 1963, p. 29).

Faulty memory?

If we grant that the New Testament was composed at an early date what about the possibility that the writers had a faulty memory of what occurred?

Since the people in the first century were not as literate as modern man, they relied more upon memory than we do today. John Warwick Montgomery makes an appropriate comment: "We know from the Mishna that it was a Jewish custom to memorize a Rabbi's teaching, for a good pupil was like 'a plastered cistern that loses not a drop' [Mishna Aboth, II.8]. And we can be sure that the early Church, impressed as it was with Jesus, governed itself by this ideal" (John Warwick Montgomery, *History and Christianity*, Downers Grove, Ill.: InterVarsity Press, 1964, pp. 37,38).

The events of the life of Christ would have made a vivid impression on all of the people who witnessed them. After one of Jesus' miracles the Bible says, "All were amazed and glorified God saying, 'We never saw anything like this!' " (Mark 2:12). Because miracles were not the norm, any extraordinary event would not soon be forgotten.

In addition, the number of eyewitnesses to the miracles of Christ were sufficient. The Apostle Paul said that the resurrection of Christ was witnessed by over five hundred people at one time (1 Corinthians 15:6).

The miracles of Jesus were done in public view as Paul told King Agrippa: "For the king, before whom I also speak freely, knows these things; for I am convinced that none of these things escapes his attention, since this thing was not done in a corner" (Acts 26:26).

It must be remembered that not all of the eyewitnesses to the biblical miracles were believers. If the disciples tended to distort the facts; the unbelieving eyewitnesses would have immediately objected.

These reasons demonstrate that the faulty memory hypothesis does not fit the facts. The New Testament was composed such a short time after the events occurred that it would be folly to assume the writers' memories were so faulty that neither they nor the unbelievers could remember the actual events of the life of Christ.

Summary and Conclusion

After reviewing some highlights of the evidence supporting the historical reliability of the New Testament, we can come to the following conclusions.

1. Archaeological and historical evidence concerning the historical events, places, and names mentioned in the New Testament conclusively affirms the basic historical reliability of the text. In addition, the nature of much of the evidence supports the biblical claim that the New Testament writers wrote during the first century and were either eyewitnesses of the events they described or had carefully checked the facts and evidence with eyewitnesses.

2. Not only are the New Testament authors accurate in their general historical observation, they also are accurate in their recording of details as the studies of Sir William Ramsay confirm.

3. If we accept the promise of Jesus Christ to send the Holy Spirit as our guide, teacher and comforter, then we should not be surprised that the Holy Spirit guided the disciples and New Testament writers. Jesus said, "But the Helper, the Holy Spirit, who the Father will send in My name, He will teach all things, and bring to your remembrance all things that I said to you" (John 14:26).

Although the Bible relates events to us that occurred thousands of years ago, the evidence clearly demonstrates that it is an accurate historical document and can be trusted as an authoritative source. The historical precision of Scripture is a true wonder.

THE WONDER OF THE BIBLE'S SCIENTIFIC RESPECTABILITY

The Lord said to Job, "Where were you when I laid the foundations of the earth? Tell me if you have understanding" (Job 38:4)

5
The Wonder Of The Bible's Scientific Respectability

The Bible was written in what is termed the pre-scientific era (before the rise of modern science). Even though it is not a scientific book, one of the wonders of the Bible is its remarkable scientific respectability.

Science—friend or enemy?

How should the Christian view science? Is science a friend or foe of the Bible? Cardinal Barberini, a friend of the astronomer Galileo, once said to him, "You teach how the heavens go; we teach how to go to heaven." The Cardinal was implying that science is neither a friend nor a foe of the Christian faith because each have different goals.

The Bible and science, however, are closely related. Scripture teaches that God created the natural order. This means that the very subject matter that the scientist studies was created by God. The Bible and science may have different goals in mind, but one cannot ignore the other.

Not mutually exclusive

Today many people believe that the Bible and science are mutually exclusive, completely contradictory to each other. Once the facts are examined, however, we will discover this is not true. Furthermore, if the God of creation also is the God of salvation, then such conflict is impossible. The same God will not create one testimony in the material record of the universe and then create a completely contradictory testimony in the written record of the Bible. Theologian Bernard Ramm writes that, "God cannot contradict His speech in Scripture. If the author of Nature and the author of Scripture are the same God, then the two books of God must eventually recite the same story. Therefore, in place of resentment or suspicion or vilification toward science and scientists, we must have a spirit of respect and gratitude . . . We are to pay due respect to both science and Scripture. Neither adoration of one nor bigoted condemnation of the other is correct. We must be ready to hear the voice of science and the voice of Scripture on common matters. The spirit of mutual respect for both science and scripture preserves us from any charge of being anti-scientific or blindly dogmatic or superstitious in our religious beliefs as they pertain to Nature" (Bernard Ramm, *The Christian View of Science and Scripture*, Grand Rapids, MI: Eerdmans, 1954, p. 25).

Science or scientism?

Though science is not in conflict with the Bible, some scientific conclusions are. The term 'scientism' often is employed by writers to describe the mindset of certain scientists who interpret their data by a particular philosophical outlook that eliminates the possibility of anything miraculous or supernatural. The job of the scientist is to test, repeat, observe, and record the data. Scientism, which goes beyond the realm of science, accepts things only on a natural order and interprets all the data in that context. However, this is not science. The scientist should construct a theory that best fits all the facts no matter what the conclusion may be. While some scientists may disagree with the Bible, the facts of science do not. Hence, science is not an enemy of Christianity.

Science and miracles

When the subject of the Bible and science is addressed, the question of miracles usually arises. Since we live in a scientific age, no longer bound by many of the superstitions of the past, some people assume that modern science has ruled out the miraculous because we now have a better understanding of how the universe functions. Unlike people of the past, we are able to explain why things happen because of our understanding of natural law.

However, natural law does not explain away the miracles recorded in the Bible. The laws that modern science has formulated do not rule out the possibility, or probability, of miracles. Scientific laws are not laws at all, but theories that are being modified from time to time as new evidence or explanations are found.

Terminology

With regard to miracles and the laws of science, many of the misconceptions have to do with terminology. A miracle may be defined simply as an event disrupting the normal order of things. We must be careful when we talk about the "laws of science." People use phrases such as "breaking the laws of science" and "unalterable scientific laws." To the nonscientist this seems as if it is something impossible to do. But this is not the case. Scientific laws are generalizations made by human observation concerning cause and effect relationships. For example, we have observed throughout history that a man who dies from crucifixion stays dead. He does not get up three days later and walk around. From this observation we formulate a law of science, namely—crucified corpses do not get up and wander around. The thought behind this and other scientific laws is that it will happen everywhere and in every case.

Normal occurrence

But a scientific law neither dictates an event nor does it explain an event. It generalizes and describes what normally occurs. Yet, the law does not predict what will always occur. If there is overwhelming evidence that on one particular occasion a crucified corpse did rise after three days, one cannot appeal to scientific law to deny the facts of the case.

Consequently, we need to be careful about using such phrases as "breaking the laws of science" when it comes to explaining unusual or miraculous events. The so-called laws are only the observations of what we, as human beings, normally see happen. They do not tell us why any event happens or that any event will always happen.

Therefore, one cannot point to the laws of science to rule out miracles. Miracles, by definition, are events that are not in the normal order of things. Scientific law does not in any way rule out the miraculous.

Bible is scientifically unique

With regard to the Bible and science, three points need to be emphasized. (1) Every ancient religion had certain unscientific views of astronomy, medicine, hygiene, etc. Ignorance and superstition were the order of the day. (2) The one notable exception is the Bible which does not contain any of the scientific absurdities that were common among their contemporaries. (3) The Scriptures were far ahead of their time in many scientific areas with which they dealt.

Scientific absurdities in ancient religions

As one might suppose, scientific beliefs in the ancient world showed a high degree of superstition. Scientific teaching in ancient religions fared no better. The Hindu Scriptures, for example, taught that the earth was riding on the back of four elephants which stood on top of a giant sea turtle swimming in a sea of milk. With one notable exception, scientific errors and absurdities were found in the religious writings of every ancient religious work.

Furthermore, the teachings concerning man and nature in many ancient religions actually hindered the development of scientific progress. When various cultures made progress in the sciences it was not reflected in their sacred books.

For example, in many sacred writings medical references are non-existent. This is because many religions taught that human life was of little or no value. Consequently there were no real medical advances made in the society. One authority on Taoism concluded that Taoist writings "hindered the progress of medicine in China for many centuries" (B. L. Gordon, *Medicine Through Antiquity* Philadelphia: F. A . Davis, 1949, p. 361) .

The religious writings of the ancient world reflected the common thought of the day. An authority on ancient oriental religions said the writers of the sacred books were, "not being advanced enough in science and culture to distinguish between the possible and impossible, almost everything which the books have to tell . . . are always reflections of prevailing opinion and of the train of thought of the time they were written" (J. J. M. deGroot, *The*

Religious System of China vol 4, 1901; reprint. Tapei: Literature House, 1964, p. ix).

The authors of the sacred writings of ancient religions reveal themselves to be imperfect humans searching for answers. There is no difference between their writings and the secular writings of the time. They all made the same mistakes.

Nothing scientifically absurd in Scripture

In dramatic contrast to primitive and mythological religious writings, the Bible is faithful to scientific evidence. The writers' observations about nature, man, and history are correct, and free from the ancient scientific inaccuracies and superstitions of their contemporaries. It is truly a wonder that the writers of Scripture did not make scientific mistakes in their observations about the world around them.

Even today, no scientific observation in the Bible contradicts known scientific evidence. However, we must emphasize that the Bible is not a scientific textbook; it is not meant to be understood only by the scientific elite.

The Bible primarily is a book about God's revelation of Himself and His dealings with mankind. Consequently, the language of Scripture is neither scientific nor unscientific, it is *nonscientific*. The language of Scripture is the language of common communication. Yet, in the ancient world, the Bible is the only religious book that has scientific credibility.

Though many ancient religions treated the universe as part of a God's nature, such teaching is not found in the Bible. C.F. Whitely writes, "The heavens were personified by the Mesopotamians as the god, Anu, and they were regarded by the Egyptians as the divine Mother; but to the Hebrews they were but one aspect of Yahweh's power and glory. The Mesopotamians again, conceived of the sun as Shamash, the god of justice; the Egyptians invested it with the properties of the divine creator; but the Hebrews merely accounted for it as one of the luminaries created by Yahweh. The moon was similarly worshipped by the Babylonians as the God Sin, and the stars were thought to determine the destiny of man; but to the Hebrews they were created by God" (C.F. Whitely, *The Genius of Ancient Israel*, Amsterdam, Philo Press, 1969, pp. 61,62).

Although errors were made by the hundreds in other religions, there are none found in Scripture. Among all the Holy Books of the world's religions, the only document that reveals an accurate understanding of science and nature is the Bible.

Far ahead of its time

The Bible is not only scientifically correct, in many areas it was far ahead of its time. When we consider the times in which the Scriptures were written and the common beliefs of the day, the fact that the Bible makes no outlandish scientific statements is even more incredible.

The writings of Moses did not reflect the widespread ignorance of Egypt in which he was raised. He did not repeat the errors that he had been schooled in since childhood.

The laws of sanitation

An example of the Bible being far ahead of the scientific knowledge of the times would be in the laws of sanitation. It was not until modern times that medical science learned the value of sanitation. The man credited with this discovery was Ingnaz Semmelweis.

Semmelweis was in charge of one of the maternity wards at the famous Vienna hospital Allegemeine, Krankenhaus, in the mid-1800s. In the hospital there was a very high mortality rate for mothers who had just given birth. No one could understand why and Semmelweis decided to investigate the problem. He noticed that more deaths were occurring from the section where the student doctors examined the mothers, than from the section where midwives worked. Semmelweis observed that the student doctors examined their patients immediately after performing autopsies on those who recently had died. The students went directly from performing the autopsies to examining the mothers without any sanitary precautions. Semmelweis instituted the rule that all doctors must first wash their hands thoroughly before going to the maternity ward. Once this new rule was instituted, the mortality rate dramatically decreased. It took some time to convince his fellow doctors that the solution to this problem was a simple matter of sanitation. Eventually he was recognized for making this important contribution.

Semmelweis rediscovered the laws of sanitation that were put down over three thousand years earlier in the Bible. Moses had commanded the people not to come into contact with anyone who had just died or anyone who was diseased. They were considered unclean. Anyone who did come in contact were commanded to wash themselves repeatedly in running water (Leviticus 13-15, Numbers 19). It is sad to think how many people needlessly died by not observing the simple sanitation procedures that are laid down in the Bible. The command, given over three thousand years ago by Moses, is just as valid today.

Water cycle and wind currents

Scripture was also accurate in determining the water cycle and the wind currents. Henry Morris explains these two phenomena: "The water cycle, whereby water is precipitated as rain or snow, then drained off by the river system into the ocean, whence it is raised by evaporation back into the skies and carried by the wind back to the land and to be again precipitated, is a fundamental fact that was strikingly set forth in the Bible ages before men discovered it. Furthermore, it is now well known that the major wind currents of the world follow well-defined circuits. These great wind currents are largely responsible for all the great ocean currents as well as the great air currents of the world. But this great truth is a matter of comparatively recent discovery . . . read Ecclesiastes 1:6-7, set down by King Solomon three thousand years ago: 'The wind goeth toward the south, and turneth about unto the north; it whirleth about continually, and the wind returneth again according to his circuits. All the rivers run into the sea; yet the sea is not full; unto the place from whence the rivers come, thither they return again.' No wonder we speak of the wisdom of Solomon! But isn't it pertinent to ask how he happened to know these things when no one else knew them until thousands of years later?" (Henry Morris, *The Bible and Modern Science*, Chicago: Moody Press, 1968, p. 7).

When speaking about areas of science, these are but three examples of the Scripture being ahead of its time. Many more illustrations could be added. It is clear the Bible is unique in this aspect among books of the ancient and modern world.

The answer?

We have discovered that the Scriptures are scientifically correct in all they state as well as ahead of their time in many areas. The fact that the Bible was written by forty different authors and all of them were scientifically correct is even more impressive. Since their view of man and nature went against the common scientific beliefs of the day, how are we to explain their accuracy?

Superior intelligence

One may argue that the Israelites were of superior intelligence to all their contemporaries. This argument falls to the ground when we examine their non-sacred writings. We find they contain the same misconceptions, the same errors and the same limited perception of their contemporaries. It is only their sacred Scriptures that are free from absurdities, not their secular writings. One cannot appeal, therefore, to their superior intellect as an answer to this question.

Lucky

Another possibility is that the biblical writers were just plain lucky, but this argument cannot be taken seriously. When we consider the fact that every biblical writer *always* was correct when he spoke of man and nature and that the Bible deals with many different authors separated by hundreds of years of time, the idea that they all could be lucky in every scientific statement is not very plausible.

Inspired by God

None of the above solutions explain the facts. The best explanation is that God supernaturally inspired the writers to avoid the common superstitions of their day. No single human author could have compiled this scientific information without the intervention of the supernatural. The Bible itself claims to be inspired by God: "All Scripture is given by inspiration of God, and is profitable for reproof, for correction, for instruction in righteousness"(2 Timothy 3:16) The word translated "inspiration" is the Greek word *theopneustos* meaning "God-breathed."

Why the apparent conflict?

If there are no genuine conflicts between science and Scripture, why do we have apparent conflicts? It must be emphasized that scientists and theologians do not work with different data. The facts are the same; the difference lies in the interpretation of the facts.

The interpretations are different, in some cases, because the presuppositions are different. For example, if an individual already has presupposed the world came into being through organic evolution, he will interpret data within the framework of his theory. The evidence will be made to fit the theory he already has accepted to be true. The same holds true for those who believe in Special Creation. Consider the following admission by scientist J.W.N. Sullivan: "It became an accepted doctrine that life never arises except from life. So far as actual evidence goes, this is still the only possible conclusion. But since it is a conclusion that seems to lead back to some supernatural creative act, it is a conclusion that scientific men find very difficult of acceptance" (J. W. N. Sullivan, *The Limitations of Science.* New York; New American Library, 1933, p. 94).

Incorrect Understanding

Other conflicts arise when there is a misunderstanding concerning what the Bible or science has said about a particular matter. Many evolutionists, who assume that creationism cannot be taken seriously, do not have a proper understanding of what the Bible says about the beginning of the universe. An example of this can be found in *Time* magazine which stated the creationist position as follows: "The earth is roughly 10,000 years old . . . the planets, stars and all living things were literally created in six days by a "Designer"; the different species of plants and animals were created, they did not evolve from any other species; a great flood was the chief force that shaped the face of the earth, in the process drowning the creatures now found as fossils" (*Time*, March 16, 1981).

The Bible, however, does not say that the world was created 4004 B.C. or that the universe is only ten thousand years old. However, most textbooks on the subject will present this as the only creationist position. The view that the earth is relatively young is only one of several possible interpretations of Genesis.

Revelation and interpretation

Unfortunately, some creationists make the mistake of believing their interpretation of Scripture is the only way it can be interpreted. Because a person believes the Genesis account of creation to be factual, it does not mean his particular interpretation of Genesis is correct. Eric Sauer comments, "We must not *a priori* equate Scripture with our exposition of it. The so-called contradictions between faith in the Bible and science are in fact not a conflict between the Bible and assured scientific knowledge, but between interpretations of the Bible and scientific theories; they offer a collision between popular traditions and philosophical speculations, which have been simply accepted from others without being tested" (Eric Sauer, *The King of the Earth*, Palm Springs, California, Ronald N. Haynes Publishers, 1981, p. 202).

Source of all error

The main reason for the seeming conflict between the Bible and science was pointed out long ago by Jesus when He told the religious leaders they were ignorant of two basic things. He said, "You are mistaken, not knowing the Scriptures or the power of God" (Matthew 22:29). A correct understanding of what the Scriptures say, and the power of the God of the Bible, would go a long way to solve the apparent conflicts between science and the Bible.

When the relationship between the Bible and science is properly understood, there is no conflict. For such an ancient book to earn scientific respectability is a true wonder.

THE WONDER OF THE BIBLE'S ABILITY TO PREDICT THE FUTURE

God has said, "I have declared the former things from the beginning; they went forth from My mouth and I caused them to hear it . . . Even from the beginning I have declared it to you; before it came to pass I proclaimed it to you" (Isaiah 48:3,5)

6
The Wonder Of The Bible's Ability To Predict The Future

Another feature that separates the Bible from any other book is its ability correctly to predict the future. Scripture contains a wealth of prophecies that were made years before they were accurately fulfilled.

The role of the biblical prophet was to act as a spokesman for God to the people. The prophet not only predicted future events in God's plan, he also exhorted and admonished the people as the Lord directed. Though his job of exhortation occupied more of his time and words than did his predictions of future events, it is with the predictive aspect of prophecy that we are concerned.

God does exist

Predictive prophecy demonstrates that God exists and that He has control of events in the past and in the future. Scripture records God saying, "I have declared the former things from the beginning; they went forth from my mouth, and I cause them to hear it. Suddenly I did them, and they came to pass . . . Even from the beginning I have declared it to you; before it came to pass I proclaimed it to you, lest you should say, 'My idol has done them, and my carved image and my molded image has commanded them' " (Isaiah 48:3,5). "Remember the former things of old, for I am God, and there is no other; I am God, and there is none like Me, declaring the end from the beginning, and from ancient times things that are not yet done" (Isaiah 46:9,10).

God knows all

The Bible records many events that were accurately predicted in advance by God. These fulfilled prophecies are evidence of God's knowledge of all things for only God, who is outside of our time-space existence and our finite knowledge, could accurately and consistently reveal the future.

The Bible says, "We also have the prophetic word made more sure, which you do well to heed as a light that shines in a dark place, until the day dawns and the morning star rises in your hearts; knowing this first, that no prophecy of Scripture is of any private interpretation, for prophecy never came by the will of man, but holy men of God spoke as they were moved by the Holy Spirit" (2 Peter 1:19-21).

Predictive prophecy is God foretelling events before they occur. Biblical predictions are not vague prophecies but are specific in nature as the following example clearly will indicate.

The Jew

One of the greatest examples of fulfilled prophecy concerns the Jew. About 4000 years ago, God called a man named Abram (later called Abraham) out from a sinful culture into a land which he had been promised.

The Bible records God making the following promises to Abraham and his descendants, "Now the Lord said to Abram: 'Get out of your country, from your kindred and from your father's house, to a land I will show you. I will make you a great nation; I will bless you and make your name great; and you shall be a blessing. I will bless those who bless you, and I will curse him who curses you; and in you all the families of the earth shall be blessed" (Genesis 12:1-3).

"And the Lord said to Abram, after Lot had separated from him: 'Lift your eyes now and look to the place where you are—northward, southward, eastward, and westward; for all the land which you see I give to you and your descendants forever. And I will make your descendants as the dust of the earth; so that if a man could number the dust of the earth, then your descendants also could be numbered. Arise and walk the land through its length and width, for I give it to you" (Genesis 13:14-17).

"And I will establish My covenant between Me and you and your descendants after you in their generations, for an everlasting covenant, to be God to you and your descendants after you. And I will give to you and your descendants after you the land in which you are a stranger, all the land of Canaan, as

an everlasting possession; and I will be their God"
(Genesis 17:7-8).

Abraham had two sons, Isaac and Ishmael. The
Lord made it clear that the promises to Abraham
would be fulfilled in his son, Isaac. God made the
following promise to Isaac: "Sojourn in this land, and I
will be with you and bless you; for to you and your
descendants I will give all of these lands; and in your
seed all the nations of the world shall be blessed"
(Genesis 26:3,4).

God later promised Isaac's son Jacob, "The land
which I gave Abraham and Isaac, I give to you; and to
your descendants after you I give this land" (Genesis
35:12).

These passages contain many specific promises.
They include:

1. A great nation will spring from Abraham.
2. Abraham's name shall be blessed.
3. He shall be a blessing to all nations.
4. Those that bless Abraham's people will be blessed.
5. Those that curse Abraham's people will be cursed.
6. His descendants, through his son Isaac, will
   inherit this promised land forever.
7. His descendants will be countless.

Further predictions

As God had promised, Abraham's descendants
multiplied. Four hundred years later they were about
to enter the land of promise. Before the nation went
into the promised land, God reconfirmed the
covenant with them:

"See, that I have set the land before you; go in and
possess the land which the LORD swore to your
fathers—to Abraham, Isaac, and Jacob—to give to
them and their descendants forever" (Deuteronomy
1:8)

God also told them about the blessings of
obedience and warned them of the consequences of
disobedience:

"If you diligently obey the voice of the Lord your
God, to observe carefully all His commandments,
which I command you today, that the Lord your God
will set you high above all nations of the earth. And all
these blessings shall come upon you and overtake

you, because you obey the voice of the Lord your God
. . . if you do not obey the voice of the Lord your God to
observe carefully all His commandments and His
statutes which I command you today, that all these
curses will come upon you and overtake you . . . Then
the Lord will scatter you among all peoples, from one
end of the earth to the other, and there you shall
serve other gods, which neither you nor your fathers
have known—wood and stone. And among those
nations you shall find no rest, nor shall the sole of
your foot have a resting place" (Deuteronomy 28:1,2,
15).

"Now it shall come to pass, when all these things
come upon you, the blessing and the curse, which I
have set before you, and you call them to mind among
all the nations where the Lord your God drives you,
and you return to the Lord your God and obey His
voice, according to all that I command you today, you
and your children, with all your heart and with all
your soul, that the Lord your God will bring you back
from captivity, and have compassion on you, and
gather you again from all the nations where the Lord
your God has scattered you" (Deuteronomy 30:1-3).

From these verses we can observe further
predictions:

8. If the people would remain faithful to God, He
would bless them and give them victory over their
enemies.

9. God would remove them from the land if they were
unfaithful to Him. They would eventually be scattered
across the whole earth as strangers in unfamiliar
lands and they would find no rest for their
wanderings.

10. However, God in His faithfulness did promise to
bring them back into the land.

From these promises God made to Abraham, we
find at least ten specific things that were predicted for
him and his offspring. As we look at the verdict of
history, we find that each of these promises has been
fulfilled wonderfully.

Fulfillment one: A great nation

A great nation did come from Abraham. By the
time they were about to enter the promised land, his

descendants in the nation Israel numbered in the millions. This is especially remarkable when we consider that Abraham and his wife Sarah were beyond the age of child bearing when their first son, Isaac, was born.

Fulfillment two: Abraham's name shall be blessed

Abraham was promised that his name should be blessed among the nations. This has been literally fulfilled. Three of the great religions of the world, Judaism, Christianity, and Islam, all look to Abraham as their human founder. His name is revered around the world.

Fulfillment three: Abraham and his descendents shall be a blessing

The descendants of Abraham shall bless the entire world. This has been literally fulfilled, both nationally and individually. One particular descendant of Abraham who fulfills this promise was Jesus Christ. The first verse of the New Testament reads, "The book of the genealogy of Jesus Christ, the Son of David, the Son of Abraham" (Matthew 1:1). The New Testament proclaims Jesus was Israel's Messiah and the Savior of the world.

The coming of Jesus Christ is the fulfillment of a specific promise God made to Abraham. The Apostle Paul wrote, "Now to Abraham and his Seed were the promises made. He does not say, 'And to the seeds,' as of many, but as of one, 'And to your Seed,' who is Christ" (Galatians 3:16).

Fulfillment four: Bless those who bless

The Bible, as well as secular history, record examples of individuals and nations who have helped Israel and found themselves blessed of God. Scripture records that God spared Rahab the harlot because she hid Israel's spies from the people of Jericho.

Fulfillment five: Curse those who curse

There also is a curse on those peoples who have attempted to destroy Israel. Not only has Israel survived, but the nations that have persecuted them—

Moab, Ammon, Edom, Philistia and many others—either have been destroyed or completely lost their individual identity.

Have you ever heard of an Austrian Amorite? A Swedish Edomite? A French Jebusite? No! These people have been totally absorbed into other cultures and races. The Jews, however, have not lost their national identity.

As the Bible predicted, all the nations that attempted to destroy Israel have been judged while those who have befriended Israel have prospered.

Fulfillment six: Descendants inherit the land

The descendants of Abraham, through his son Isaac, did inherit the land of promise. Four hundred years after God spoke to Abraham, a nation of several million entered into the promised land. Today they still are there, thousands of years after the initial promise.

Fulfillment seven: Countless numbers

The number of Abraham's descendants have become countless as predicted in Scripture. They have numbered in the tens of millions and are continuing to this day. This is remarkable when we consider again that Abraham and Sarah's first child, Isaac, was born after both of them were beyond the child-bearing age.

Fulfillment eight: Blessings for obedience

God had promised blessings for His people as long as they remained obedient to Him. The Old Testament records times of great prosperity when Israel was faithful to the Lord. During the reign of David and Solomon, for example, the borders increased and the people were mightily blessed of God.

Fulfillment nine: God will remove them for disobeying

If they were unfaithful, God promised to remove them from the land. This has been literally fulfilled. In 721 B.C. the Assyrians removed the Northern kingdom of Israel into captivity. In 606 B.C. King Nebuchadnezzar took the remainder of the people captive to Babylon. In 588-586 B.C., after a long siege, he burned the city and the temple.

The children of Israel also were scattered in A.D. 70 when Titus the Roman surrounded the city of Jerusalem and burned the rebuilt city and the temple. For almost 1900 years, the Jews wandered about the earth as strangers being persecuted from every side. The culmination of their persecution occurred in the holocaust of World War II, when 6 million Jews were put to death in concentration camps. The predictions again were literally fulfilled.

Fulfillment ten: God will bring them back

However, as God promised, He allowed those who desired to return to the land. In 537-536 B.C., or after seventy years, those who had been taken captive to Babylon were allowed to return (Ezra chapter 1).

Though removed from their homeland a second time in A.D. 70, again the people returned. Against all odds, the state of Israel was reborn on May 14, 1948, and the Jews began to return to their homeland from all points of the compass. This is the second time in their history since becoming a nation, that they have come back into their land after being forcibly removed.

Since 1948 they have survived some terrible conflicts, including the Six-Day War in 1967 and the 1973 Holy Day War. Conflicts continue to this day, yet they still survive.

Through all of this, the nation neither perished nor lost its national identity. History has demonstrated that any people who leave their homeland will, after about five generations, lose their national identity by being absorbed into a new culture, but the Jews remained a distinct entity.

Middle East expert Lance Lambert comments on the unique experiences of the Jews. "God has dealt with no nation as he has dealt with the Jewish people. In their 4,000-year-long history, they have been exiled from their land twice, and have been restored to it twice . . .

"No other nation in the history of mankind has twice been uprooted from its land, scattered to the ends of the earth and then brought back again to that same territory. If the first exile and restoration were remarkable, the second is miraculous. Israel has twice lost its statehood and its national sovereignty, twice had its capital and hub of religious life destroyed, its towns and cities razed to the ground, its people deported and dispersed, and then twice had it restored again.

"Furthermore, no other nation or ethnic group has been scattered to the four corners of the earth, and yet survived as an easily identifiable and recognizable group . . . From the Far East to the Far West there is hardly a nation that has not had Jewish citizens within it. The remarkable fact is that the Jewish people have been able to survive as a people, instead of being absorbed and assimilated into the larger Gentile majorities among whom it was scattered. We must remember that we are not considering a period of one generation, or even one century, but nearly two thousand years" (Lance Lambert, *Israel,* Wheaton, Illinois, Tyndale, 1981, pp. 55,56).

Living miracle

I was once attending a debate at a California college concerning the person of Jesus Christ. Among the participants was a rabbi. During the question period the rabbi was asked why he didn't believe in Jesus. He replied, "I don't believe in the New Testament miracles."

A student immediately asked him why he rejected the New Testament miracles but accepted the Old Testament miracles. The rabbi said, "I don't believe in the Old Testament miracles either, I believe they are all myths."

It was unbelievable to hear someone make such a statement. The mere fact that he, as a Jew, had survived, is one of the greatest miracles of all history.

Mark Twain wrote the following insightful comment: "If the statistics are right, the Jews constitute but one per cent of the human race. It suggests a nebulous dim puff of star dust lost in the blaze of the Milky Way. Properly the Jew ought hardly to be heard of; but he is heard of. He is as prominent on the planet as any other people, and his commercial importance is extravagantly out of proportion to the smallness of his bulk. His contributions to the world's list of great names in literature, science, art, music, finance, medicine . . . are also way out of proportion to the weakness of his numbers. He has made a marvelous fight in this world, in all the ages; and has done it with his hands tied behind him. He could be vain of himself, and be excused for it. The Egyptian, the Babylonian and the Persian rose, filled the planet with sound and splendour, then faded to dream-stuff and passed away; the Greek and the Roman followed, and made a vast noise, and they are gone; other peoples have sprung up and held their torch high for a time, but it burned out, and they sit in twilight now, or have vanished. The Jew saw them all beat them all, and is now what he always was, exhibiting no decadence, no infirmities of age, no weakening of parts, no slowing of his energies, no dulling of his alert and aggressive mind. All things are mortal but the Jew; all other forces pass, but he remains. What is the secret of his immortality?" (Mark Twain *Concerning the Jews*, 1899).

The God of Scripture is faithful. He has demonstrated His existence and faithfulness by dealing with the nation Israel as a living sign to the world that He keeps His promises.

Fulfilled biblical prophecy is convincing evidence of God's knowledge of all things—past, present, and future. It is indeed one of the wonders of the Bible.

THE WONDER OF THE BIBLE'S HONESTY

"God . . . cannot lie" (Titus 1:2)

7
The Wonder Of The Bible's Honesty

The seventh feature that separates the Bible from all other books is its honesty. Scripture honestly deals with the frailties of the people of God and even with the shortcomings of its own authors. The Bible paints a realistic portrait of its characters, resisting any temptation to mythologize, deify, or perfect them.

Noah

The Bible lists Noah as a man of great faith. He believed God's promise and helped save part of humanity from the Great Flood. However, after the Flood, Noah was once found in a drunken stupor, "Then Noah began farming and planted a vineyard. And He drank of the wine and became drunk, and uncovered himself inside his tent. And Ham, the father of Canaan, saw the nakedness of his father, and told his two brothers outside. But Shem and Japeth took a garment and laid it upon both their shoulders and walked backward and covered the nakedness of their father; and their faces were turned away, so that they did not see their father's nakedness" (Genesis 9:20-23).

The same man who trusted God to save humanity through the ark allowed himself to drink to excess. Rather than omitting this episode, Scripture shows that Noah was a man of like passions as you and I.

Abraham

Though Abraham was called the "father of the faithful," he had his lapses of faith. The Bible says, "And Abraham said of Sarah his wife, 'She is my sister.' So Abimelech king of Gerar sent and took Sarah. But God came to Abimelech in a dream of the night, and said to him, 'Behold, you are a dead man because of the woman whom you have taken, for she is married.' . . . Then Abimelech called Abraham and said to him, 'What have you done to us? And how I have sinned against you, that you have brought on me and on my kingdom a great sin? You have done to me things that ought not to be done" (Genesis 20:2,3,9).

Though many righteous deeds of Abraham are recorded in Scripture, so is his sin.

David

The Bible says that King David was a man after God's own heart. Yet, the Scripture also testifies that he was a murderer and adulterer. The Bible says, "So David sent and inquired about the woman. And one said, 'Is this not Bathsheba, the daughter of Eliam, the wife of Uriah the Hittite?' And David sent messengers and took her, and when she came to him, he lay with her; and when she had purified herself from her uncleanness, she returned to her house . . . Now it came about in the morning that David wrote a letter to Joab, and sent it by the hand of Uriah. And he had written in a letter saying, 'Place Uriah in the front line of the fiercest battle and withdraw from him, so that he may be struck down and die' " (2 Samuel 11:3,4,14,15).

David was punished for his sin and paid a severe price for his deeds. His murder and adultery were not whitewashed for the record.

Disciples of Jesus

Though the disciples of Jesus Christ helped turn the world upside down by proclaiming the message of the risen Savior, they often fell into sin. The Bible does not overlook their faults. When Jesus was about to die the Bible says, "there arose a dispute among them as to which one of them was regarded to be greatest" (Luke 22: 24). At Jesus' most troubling hour His disciples were insensitive to the events that were transpiring.

Apostle Paul

The Apostle Paul, the man who wrote many of the New Testament books, had a huge argument with his companion, Barnabas: "And after some days, Paul said to Barnabas, 'Let us return and visit the brethren in every city in which we proclaimed the word of the Lord, and see how they are.' And Barnabas was desirous of taking John, called Mark, along with them also. But Paul kept insisting that they should not be taking John, called Mark, along who had deserted them in Pamphylia and had not gone with them to the work. And there arose such a sharp disagreement that they separated from one another, and Barnabas took Mark with him and sailed away to Cyprus" (Acts 15:36-39).

The fact that the characters in the Bible fell into sin does not detract from the biblical message. On the contrary, the clear message of Scripture is that all of us have sinned and fallen short of the perfect standard of God. The Bible proclaims the holiness of the Lord God, not the perfection of His followers and prophets.

Jesus

There is one notable exception. The same authors who honestly depicted their own sin testified there was one among them who was sinless—Jesus Christ our Lord. Scripture makes it clear that Jesus was without sin.

When we talk about sin we are referring to breaking the law of God. If Jesus had broken the law in any respect then He would be a sinner. The Bible, however, says that Jesus never once sinned. This is verified by His own testimony, the testimony of His friends, the testimony of His enemies, and the testimony of God the Father.

Jesus' own testimony

As we examine the account of the life of Jesus, as recorded in the New Testament, we observe that He believed Himself to be without sin. When He came to be baptized by John the Baptist, Jesus was momentarily stopped because John realized it was unnecessary. John's baptism was for the confession of sin, and he realized that this one had no sin. But Jesus insisted upon being baptized. " 'Permit it to be now, for thus it is fitting for us to fulfill all righteousness.' Then He allowed Him" (Matthew 3:15).

Jesus submitted to the baptism but did not confess sin.

Immediately after His baptism He was tempted by Satan. Yet Jesus refused to give in to the temptation and told the devil, "Away with you, Satan! For it is written, 'You shall worship the Lord your God, and Him only you shall serve' " (Matthew 4:10). In the great spiritual battle with the devil, Jesus did not succumb to sin.

Throughout His ministry Jesus challenged those with Him to find sin in His life. "Which of you convicts Me of sin?" (John 8:46). The response from those surrounding Him was silence. They had never seen Him sin, for He had not sinned.

At the end of His life, while proceeding to the Garden of Gethsemane to be betrayed by Judas Iscariot, Jesus prayed to His heavenly Father saying, "I have glorified You on the earth. I have finished the work which You have given Me to do" (John 17:4).

Knowing of His impending death, His prayer was not one of confession, but rather one of victory. He had finished the mission given to Him by the Father and had finished it without committing a sin.

The testimony of His friends

Not only did Jesus recognize that He was sinless, those who knew Him were aware of the fact. The Scripture records the attitude of the disciples toward Jesus. They make it clear He was sinless.

Peter wrote, "Who committed no sin, nor was guile found in His mouth" (1 Peter 2:22). The Apostle John testified, "And you know that He was manifested to take away our sins, and in Him there is no sin" (1 John 3:5). The Apostle Paul reported, "For He made Him who knew no sin to be sin for us, that we might become the righteousness of God in Him" (2 Corinthians 5:21).

The testimony is especially significant because it was given by some of the very same people who were constantly with Jesus. They saw Him when He was tired, they saw Him when He was hungry, they saw Him when the multitudes pressed around Him. Yet they testified that in all this they never once had seen Him sin. Their testimony, that He was without sin, carries considerable weight because they honestly reported their own faults and shortcomings.

The testimony of His enemies

We have heard the testimony of Jesus Himself along with the testimony of His friends with regard to His sinlessness. Yet there is another factor to be considered—His enemies. Those who did not believe in Him also gave testimony to the fact that He was sinless. As He was casting an evil spirit out of a man this spirit gave testimony to Jesus saying, "What have we to do with You, Jesus of Nazareth? Did you come to destroy us? I know who You are—the Holy One of God!" (Mark 1:24).

When the traitor Judas Iscariot realized the awful deed which he had done in betraying Jesus he returned to the chief priests and elders saying, "I have sinned by betraying innocent blood" (Matthew 27:4).

At Jesus' trial those intimately involved in the proceedings admitted they could find no fault in Him. "Now the chief priests, the elders, and all the council sought false testimony against Jesus to put Him to death, but found none. Even though many false witnesses came forward, they found none" (Matthew 26:59,60).

Pontius Pilate, upon examining Jesus, also testified he could find no fault with Him. "And when he had said this, he went out again to the Jews, and said to them, 'I find no fault in Him at all' " (John 18:38).

When Jesus died upon the cross, the Roman centurion who was watching the proceedings made the following observation: "Certainly this was a righteous Man!" (Luke 23:47).

It is one thing that Jesus' friends recognized His sinlessness; it is quite another thing that His enemies also acknowledged He was without sin.

The testimony of God the Father

The final and by far the most significant testimony that Jesus was sinless came from God the Father.

At Jesus' baptism the Father voiced His pleasure of the Son: "And the Holy Spirit descended in bodily form like a dove upon Him, and a voice from heaven which said, 'You are My beloved Son; in You I am well pleased' " (Luke 3:22).

which said, 'You are My beloved Son; in You I am well pleased' " (Luke 3:22).

Later in His ministry, at the Transfiguration, the Father again voiced audibly that the Son had pleased Him. "While he was still speaking, behold a bright cloud overshadowed them; and suddenly a voice came out of the cloud saying, 'This is My beloved Son, in whom I am well pleased. Hear Him!' " (Matthew 17:5).

On another occasion, before the multitude, the Father testified to the ministry of the Son: " 'Father, glorify Your name.' Then a voice came from heaven saying, 'I have both glorified it and will glorify it again' " (John 12:28).

The final act that demonstrated the testimony of God the Father to the sinlessness of Jesus was the acceptance of His sacrifice on the cross. The fact that He received Jesus into heaven showed that His mission was accomplished as the perfect, sinless sacrifice. Jesus' last words were, "Father, into Your hands I commend My spirit" (Luke 23:46). If Jesus had sinned in any manner He would not have been able to appear in the presence of His Father. The Father's unqualified acceptance of Jesus was the final testimony to His sinlessness.

Thus we know that Jesus Himself, His friends, His enemies, and God the Father all considered Him to be without sin. This being the case we conclude that Jesus lived a perfect, sinless life while here on earth.

Conclusion

Bible teacher Wilbur Smith offers a fitting observation, "Fifteen million minutes of life on this earth, in the midst of a wicked and corrupt generation—every thought, every deed, every purpose, every work, privately and publicly, from the time He opened His baby eyes until He expired on the cross, were all approved of God. Never once did our Lord have to confess any sin, for He had no sin" (Wilbur Smith, *Have You Considered Him?* Downers Grove, IL: Inter-Varsity Press, 1970, p. 8, 9).

The honesty of the Bible is refreshing. The faults of its characters (except for the sinless Son of God) are not overlooked or whitewashed. This honesty is another of the wonders which set the Bible apart from all other literature.

THE WONDER OF THE BIBLE'S UNIQUE TEACHINGS

"'You are My witnesses,' says the Lord, 'and My
servant whom I have chosen, that you may know and
believe Me, and understand that I am He. Before Me
there was no God formed, nor shall there be after Me'"
(Isaiah 43:10)

8
The Wonder Of The Bible's Unique Teachings

Another aspect of the Bible that separates it from other religious books is its unique teachings. The teachings of Scripture cannot be explained as a product of the religious environment of its authors, since many of its teachings were contrary to the religious beliefs at that time. When the teachings of Scripture are compared to other ancient religions they are found to be one of a kind, having no like or equal.

We will examine three of the many unique teachings of Scripture: the belief in one God; the teaching of a loving Father God; and a realistic hope of life beyond the grave.

One God

Against a world that accepted the existence of many gods, the Bible consistently, from beginning to end, proclaims the existence of only one God. The nation Israel was surrounded by cultures that were polytheists (believers in more than one God). Yet, the Old Testament is filled with warnings against idolatry and with condemnation of idolators.

The Bible repeatedly emphasizes belief in one God: "Hear O Israel! The Lord is our God, the Lord is one! And you shall love the Lord your God with all your heart and with all your souls and with all your might" (Deuteronomy 6:4).

"You are My witnesses, declares the Lord, and My servant whom I have chosen, in order that you may know and believe Me, and understand that I am He. Before Me there was no God formed, and there will be none after Me. I, even I, am the Lord; and there is no savior besides Me" (Isaiah 43:10).

The New Testament continues in the proclamation that only one God exists: "We know that there is no such thing as an idol in the world, and that there is no God but one. For even if there are so-called gods whether in heaven or on earth, as indeed there are many gods and many lords, yet for us there is but one God, the Father, from whom are all things, and we exist for Him; and one Lord Jesus Christ, through who are all things, and we exist through Him" (1 Corinthians 8:4-6).

The message of Scripture is that only one God exists, all others are only pretenders.

No idols

In contrast to the other nations of the ancient world, Scripture forbids believers to make images of the one true God: "You shall not make for yourself any carved image, or any likeness of anything that is in heaven above, or that is in the earth beneath, or that is in the water under the earth; you shall not bow down to them" (Exodus 20:4,5). The God of Israel would not permit anyone to make a likeness of Him.

Personal and loving Father

The nature and attributes of the God of the Bible also are different from the concepts of God or gods in other cultures with whom Israel had contact. The Bible reveals a God who is infinite and personal, who cares for human beings as a loving Father. He has the characteristics of a person.

A person can be defined as someone who is rational, conscious of his own being. This is how the Bible portrays God. He is a person, not an impersonal force. The Bible speaks of Him as the living God: "But the Lord is the true God; He is the living God and the everlasting King" (Jeremiah 10:10).

The Scriptures attribute characteristics to God that can be only those of a person.

The Bible speaks of God having the capacity to love: "The Lord has appeared of old to me, saying: 'Yes I have loved you with an everlasting love' " (Jeremiah 31:3). "But God demonstrates His own love toward us, in that while we were still sinners, Christ died for us" (Romans 5:8).

God also can show anger: "And the Lord said to Moses . . . 'Now therefore, let Me alone, that My wrath may burn hot against them and I may consume them' " (Exodus 32:10,11).

The Scriptures teach that God has the ability to show mercy: "Then God saw their works, that they turned from their evil way; and God relented from the disaster that He had said He would bring upon them, and He did not do it" (Jonah 3:10).

The Bible speaks of God as wanting or desiring things: "The Lord is not slack concerning His promise, as some count slackness, but is longsuffering toward us, not willing that any should perish but that all should come to repentance" (2 Peter 3:9).

The Bible says that God has an intellect. He has a mind that thinks. God uses His mind to instruct His people concerning what they should do: "Thus says the Lord, your Redeemer, the Holy One of Israel: 'I am the Lord your God who teaches you to profit, who leads you by the way you should go' " (Isaiah 48:17).

These are some of the attributes that the Bible says God possesses. They are all consistent with personhood. By demonstrating these in His character God has shown that He is a personal God.

The Bible also contrasts the personal living God to idols, which neither hear nor speak. The Apostle Paul told a crowd at Lystra: "Men, why are you doing these things? We also are men with the same nature as you, and preach to you that you should turn from these vain things to the living God, who made the heaven, the earth, the sea, and all things in them" (Acts 14:15).

When he wrote to the church at Thessalonica Paul again brought out the distinction between the living God and non-living idols: "For they themselves declare concerning us what manner of entry we had to you, and how you turned to God from idols to serve the living and true God" (1 Thessalonians 1:9).

Hence the Bible contrasts the living God who hears, sees, thinks, feels, and acts like a person with idols which are things, not personal.

The God of Scripture personifies love, respect, justice, and mercy. This is in contrast to other gods of the ancient world who were to be obeyed and served out of fear rather than from loving respect.

An idea of the fatherly attitude of the God of the Bible is revealed by Jesus Christ: "And I say to you, ask, and it shall be given you; seek, and you shall find; knock, and it shall be opened to you. For everyone who asks, receives; and he who seeks finds; and to him who knocks, it shall be opened. Now suppose one of your fathers is asked by his son for a fish; he will not give him a snake instead of a fish, will he? Or if he is asked for an egg, he will not give him a scorpion, will he? If you then, being evil, know how to give good gifts to your children, how much more shall your heavenly Father give the Holy Spirit to those who ask Him"? (Luke 11:9-13).

In many non-Christian religions, the God who is served is obeyed out of fear. The Bible tells believers to obey God out of their love for Him, Jesus said, "If you love Me, you will keep My commandments" (John 14:15).

Life beyond the grave

All of us have to face the fact that we eventually will die. What happens to a person after death? The writer of Ecclesiastes, like the rest of us, wondered about what happens to people when they die: "For what happens to the sons of men also happens to beasts; one thing befalls them: as one dies, so dies the other, surely, they all have one breath; man has no advantage over beasts, for all is vanity. All go to one place: all are from the dust, and all return to dust" (Ecclesiastes 3:19-20).

Most religions deal with the question of life beyond the grave. To some, this life is all that there is. A study of God's Word, the Bible, reveals that death is not the end of existence, it is just the beginning of eternity. There is hope of eternal life for those who die.

A realistic hope

From an observational point of view we do not know what happens to a person after he dies. We bury his body and it returns to dust. Someone once observed that, "Man can live forty days without food, about three days without water, about eight minutes without air . . . but only about one second without hope."

The thing that separates the Bible from other religious books is that it provides a realistic hope for those who have died. It is based upon the promise of Jesus Christ. Jesus promised everlasting life to those who believe in Him. "Because I live, you will live also" (John 14:19).

Based on resurrection

The basis of this promise is the bodily resurrection of Jesus Christ. The Apostle Peter, speaking fifty days after the Passover of Jesus' death, declared: "Men of Israel, hear these words: Jesus of Nazareth, a Man attested by God to you by miracles, wonders, and signs which God did through Him in your midst, as you yourselves also know— Him, being delivered by the determined counsel and foreknowledge of God, you have taken by lawless hands, have crucified, and put to death; whom God raised up, having loosed the pains of death, because it was not possible that He should be held by it" (Acts 2:22-24).

The unanimous testimony of the New Testament is that Jesus rose from the dead and appeared to many people after His death. These individuals provide eyewitness testimony of the fact of His resurrection.

Hope for the dead

The Apostle Paul wrote to the church at Thessalonica regarding the state of those who had died: "But I do not want you to be ignorant, brethren, concerning those who have fallen asleep, lest you sorrow as others who have no hope. For if we believe that Jesus died and rose again, even so God will bring with Him those who sleep in Jesus" (1 Thessalonians 4:13,14).

The Apostle Paul says it is proper for people to sorrow for those who have died. But we are not to sorrow as the unbelievers do for we have a hope beyond the grave.

The Bible promises a new body for those who trust God: "For we know that if our earthly house, this tent, is destroyed, we have a building from God, a house not made with hands, eternal in the heavens" (2 Corinthians 5:1). "For this corruptible must put on incorruption, and this mortal must put on immortality" (1 Corinthians 15:53).

Because the Bible promises eternal life in God's presence for those who trust Christ there are things people can do to prepare for death. The first step is obvious. Preparation for death and eternal life requires faith in Jesus Christ.

The believer can then prepare for death by realizing that God has a purpose and a plan for his life. The psalmist trusted God to be with Him through the experience of life as well as death: "Yea, though I walk through the valley of the shadow of death, I will fear no evil; for you are with me " (Psalm 23:4).

The belief in one God, the idea of God as a personal, loving Father, and a genuine hope beyond the grave are three of many of the unique beliefs found in the Scripture. The Bible, in both Old and New Testaments, contains teachings that are unique and wonderful in comparison to the best teachings offered in any other religious or non-religious writings.

THE WONDER OF THE BIBLE'S MAIN CHARACTER— JESUS CHRIST

"No man ever spoke like this Man" (John 7:46)

9
The Wonder Of The Bible's Main Character— Jesus Christ

We have already seen that the Bible is Christ-centered; its all about Him. We have also noted that the accounts in Scripture are trustworthy; the text has been accurately transmitted and the history that the Bible records is precise. The ninth wonder under consideration concerns the person and work of Jesus Christ. When one examines the life and teachings of Jesus it becomes clear that He is in a class by Himself.

Purpose of His coming

The great truth revealed in the New Testament is that the eternal God became one of us; He became a human being: "And the Word became flesh and dwelt among us, and we beheld His glory, the glory as of the only begotten of the Father, full of grace and truth" (John 1:14).

The Apostle Paul echoes John's thoughts: "Who, being in the form of God, did not consider it robbery to be equal with God, but made Himself of no reputation, taking the form of a servant, and coming in the likeness of men" (Philippians 2:6,7). In becoming a man Jesus laid aside His heavenly glory to live among us. The question is, "Why did He do it?" There are four main reasons:

To reveal God to mankind

The first and foremost reason was to reveal God to mankind. If you wish to know what God is like you need go no further than to look at Jesus. "No one has seen God at any time. The only begotten Son, who is in the bosom of the Father, He has declared Him" (John 1:18). This verse teaches that Jesus explained

God to humanity. No longer do we need to wonder what God is like; Jesus shows us.

To die for the sins of the world

Another reason for Christ's coming was to die on the cross for the sins of the world: "Just as the Son of Man did not come to be served, but to serve, and to give His life a ransom for many" (Matthew 20:28). His death on the cross paid the penalty for our sins. He died in our place so that we do not have to suffer eternally for our misdeeds.

To destroy the works of the devil

He came also to destroy the works of the devil and the hold he has had over mankind: "For this purpose the Son of God was manifested, that He might destroy the works of the devil" (1 John 3:8).

Jesus' death on the cross frees us from the power of sin. The devil no longer has any right to control us because Christ has given us the freedom to choose not to sin.

An example

Jesus also came to provide an example for the believer on how to live one's life. When a person puts his faith in Christ he has an example to follow. Jesus lived the perfect life as the perfect man with faith in His Father. Consequently we are told "to walk just as He walked" (1 John 2:6).

It is for these reasons that Jesus left heaven's glory to live as one of us.

Different from other religious leaders

Throughout history many religious leaders have come on the scene and have attracted large followings. The Buddha, with his teachings on how to cope with life's suffering, gained millions of adherents. Confucius, with his precepts on how members of society should get along with each other, likewise numbers his followers in the millions. The same can be said for Muhammad and the Islamic religion. Yet, Jesus has demonstrated that He is in a different class from all other religious leaders.

He is the issue

Several things make Jesus different. First, Jesus made Himself the issue while other leaders made their teachings the issue. Central to religions such as Buddhism, Islam, Sikhism, Confucianism, etc. are the teachings. What is stressed is what the leaders taught, not so much who they were. The teachers, therefore, are secondary to the teachings.

However, in Christianity, the reverse is true. The all-important issue is not so much what Jesus taught as who He claimed to be. The religious leaders of His day became infuriated when He claimed authority over everything. When Jesus healed on the Sabbath, contrary to their tradition, they became incensed: "Therefore some of the Pharisees said, 'This Man is not from God because He does not keep the Sabbath.' Others said, 'How can a man who is a sinner do such signs?' And there was division among them" (John 9:16). Jesus answered this charge by declaring, "For the Son of Man is Lord even of the Sabbath" (Matthew 12:8).

This is one major difference between Jesus and the other religious leaders—He made Himself the issue. "He asked His disciples, saying, 'Who do men say that I, the Son of Man, am' " (Matthew 16:13). He asked this question to secure a commitment either for Him or against Him. We do not find the leaders of the other world religions doing such a thing.

Demonstrated authority

Another aspect that separates Jesus from other religious leaders is that He demonstrated He had authority to make such monumental claims. While other religious leaders have made claims, they gave no legitimate evidence to substantiate them. Jesus, on the other hand, backed up His claims with miracles.

The account of Jesus healing the paralyzed man illustrates this point. When the paralyzed man was brought before Him, Jesus said, "Son, your sins are forgiven you" (Mark 2:5).

This claim to forgive sins upset the religious rulers: "But some of the scribes were sitting there and reasoning in their hearts, 'Why does this Man speak blasphemies like this? Who can forgive sins but God alone?' " (Mark 2:6,7).

They were absolutely right in their assertion that only God could forgive sins. But making the claim to forgive sins is something that cannot be openly verified. How could anyone have known that Jesus had this authority?

Knowing this to be the case, Jesus responded, 'Why do you reason about these things in your hearts? Which is easier to say to the paralytic, 'Your sins are forgiven you,' or to say, 'Arise, take up your bed and walk?' But that you may know that the Son of Man has power on earth to forgive sins'— He said to the paralytic, 'I say to you arise, take up your bed and, and go your way to your house.' And immediately he arose, took up the bed, and went out in the presence of them all" (Mark 2:8-12).

Notice how Jesus dealt with the situation. He asked, "Which is easier to say, your sins are forgiven or rise up and walk?" It is easier to say your sins are forgiven because no one can tell at that moment whether or not they have been forgiven. The forgiveness of sin is not accompanied by some observable sign. But, if someone says to a paralytic, "Rise up and walk," immediately it will become apparent whether or not he has any authority. By healing the paralytic, Jesus showed the religious rulers He had the power over sickness in the natural realm. This illustrated that He also had authority in the unseen realm to forgive sin.

Other religious leaders might have claimed monumental things, but they never gave any signs to back up their claims. Jesus not only made the claims, He backed them up with observable miracles which showed He had the authority to make them.

Conquered death

A final fact which separates Jesus from other religious leaders is that He conquered the ultimate enemy that all of us face, death. By coming back from the dead, He provided a concrete answer to the question, "What will happen to us when we die?" No other religious leader has returned from the dead to verify His claims except Jesus of Nazareth. The evidence that Jesus came back from the dead is sufficient to convince even the most skeptical. The English legal expert, Lord Darling, concluded after examining the evidence for Jesus' resurrection: "We as Christians, are asked to take a very great deal on trust; the teachings, for example, and the miracles of Jesus. If we had to take all on trust, I, for one, should be skeptical. The crux of the problem of whether Jesus was, or was not, what he proclaimed himself to be, must surely depend upon the truth or otherwise of the resurrection. On that greatest point we are not merely asked to have faith. In its favour as a living truth there exists such overwhelming evidence, positive and negative, factual and circumstantial, that no intelligent jury in the world can fail to bring in a verdict that the resurrection story is true" (Lord Darling cited by Michael Green, *The Day Death Died*, Intervarsity Press, 1982, p. 15).

No other major religious leader has a resurrection claimed for him. In addition, the bodily resurrection of Jesus can be *tested* by the most rigorous historical methods. While many other religious traditions have an idea of spirit resurrections (untestable hypothesis), only the Bible proclaims a bodily resurrection that passes all tests of historical reliability. This provides the believer with a genuine hope of life beyond the grave.

The resurrection of Jesus Christ separates Him from all other religious leaders, past or present for He conquered the greatest enemy we all face—death.

Jesus-the only

Carnegie Simpson offers a fitting conclusion on the uniqueness of Jesus: "Instinctively we do not class Him with others. When one reads His name in a list beginning with Confucius and ending with Goethe we feel it is an offense less against orthodoxy than against decency. Jesus is not one of the group of the world's great. Talk about Alexander the Great and Charles the Great and Napoleon the Great if you will . . . Jesus is apart. He is not the Great; He is the Only. He is simply Jesus. Nothing could add to that . . . He is beyond our analyses. He confounds our canons of human nature. He . . . awes our spirits" (Quoted by John Stott, *Basic Christianity*, Downers Grove, Ill: Inter-Varsity Press, 1971, p. 36).

The matchless character of Jesus Christ is a true wonder of the Bible.

THE WONDER OF THE BIBLE'S LIFE-CHANGING MESSAGE

"Therefore if the Son makes you free, you shall be free indeed" (John 8:36)

10
The Wonder Of The Bible's Life-Changing Message

As we have examined the facts, we have discovered that the hope the Bible offers is genuine. Unlike other religions and religious books, the faith that the Bible calls for is backed up by facts that can be put to the test. We now arrive at the last of the ten wonders of the Bible which personalizes the evidence we have examined. If the Bible is indeed the Word of God, it should demonstrate an ability to transform lives.

Christian scholar Bernard Ramm gives this perspective on the life-changing importance of Scripture: "Whatever passes as true must have direct tangency with life and experience . . . It is to be questioned if Christianity would have had the hold it has had, and does have on hundreds of thousands of people if it lacked direct tangency with life and experience even though it created such an imposing theological and philosophical edifice. Because Christianity is true it must have relevancy to every significant aspect of the universe and human experience. It must not only provide us with the materials of a great philosophy . . . but it must have a relevancy . . . to human experience" (Bernard Ramm, *Protestant Christian Evidences,* Chicago, Il, Moody Press, 1953, p. 208).

The Bible claims that its message can fill the spiritual void that is within all of us. Jesus said, "Come to Me, all you who labor and are heavy laden, and I will give you rest" (Matthew 11:28).

Scripture invites us to believe and see for ourselves: "Oh, taste and see that the Lord is good; Blessed is the man who trusts in Him" (Psalm 34:8).

Jesus Christ has demonstrated that He is the eternal God who became a human being. His death on the cross for the sins of the world offers a deliverance from sin and its effects. Whether or not a person believes this, it is still true. Jesus Christ is the Lord of the universe. When anyone believes in Jesus as His Savior, his outlook on life takes on a new perspective—he becomes a "new creation" (2 Corinthians 5:17) and life becomes more meaningful. Jesus touches us in our practical, daily living. He strikes at the very center of our existence. Belief in Jesus gives the individual a genuine identity, purpose, and destiny.

Identity

Belief in Jesus solves our identity problem. We no longer wonder who we are. We now realize that we are men and women created in the image of God. This means we have the ability to think, love and communicate. We have the chance to know God because He has given us these abilities. We now know who we are.

Purpose

Along with identity come a purpose for living. Instead of living life aimlessly we can now know the reason we have been created—to love God and enjoy Him forever. God has provided in the Bible a guide on how we are to live and what He requires of us. By believing in Jesus we now have purpose. We not only know who we are, we know why we are here.

Destiny

Finally, belief in Jesus provides us with a destiny. We know that this life is not all there is. We are beings made for eternity, and belief in Jesus allows us to spend eternity in the presence of God. Thus, the grave has no ultimate terror for us because we know there is a better existence beyond this life. Belief in Jesus gives us a destiny. We now know where we are going when we die and we have a genuine hope for a better life.

Consequences of rejecting Christ

Many have the impression that Jesus only talked about the love of God and never about judgment. In no uncertain terms, however, His message included warnings of punishment for those who rejected His claims. Those who reject Christ will spend eternity separated from God.

The toughest words of judgment that are recorded in the Bible come from the lips of Jesus. He had this to say to the hypocritical religious rulers: "But woe to you, scribes and Pharisees, hypocrites! For you shut up the kingdom of heaven against men; for you neither go in yourselves, nor do you allow those who are entering to go in" (Matthew 23:13); "Serpents, brood of vipers! How can you escape the condemnation of hell?" (Matthew 23:33).

Jesus said that those who do not put their faith in Him will suffer the consequences: "Therefore I said to you that you will die in your sins; for if you do not believe that I am He, you will die in your sins" (John 8:24).

When Jesus comes back to the earth to judge the nations, He will say to those who do not believe, "Depart from Me, you cursed, into the everlasting fire prepared for the devil and his angels" (Matthew 25:41).

From these statements we see that Jesus talked about God's punishment for those who do not accept Him as Savior. He said there is a place of judgment where unbelievers will be eternally separated from God. This is in contrast to those who do believe. They will be forever in God's presence and enjoy God's unending blessings.

Has He changed your life?

In the last two thousand years, millions of people have been transformed by the life-changing message of Scripture and encounter with the person of Jesus Christ the Savior.

Secular psychiatrist J. T. Fisher explains it this way: "If you were to take the sum total of all authoritative articles ever written by the most qualified of psychologists and psychiatrists on the subject of mental hygiene—if you were to combine them and refine them and cleave out all the excess verbiage . . . and if you were to have these unadulterated bits of pure scientific knowledge concisely expressed by the most capable of living poets, you would have an awkward and incomplete summation of the Sermon on the Mount. And it would suffer immeasurably through comparison. For nearly two thousand years the Christian world has been holding in its hands the complete answer to its restless and fruitless yearnings. Here . . . rests the blueprint for successful human life with optimism, mental health, and contentment" (J. T. Fisher and L. S. Hawley, *A Few Buttons Missing.* Philadelphia, Lippincott, 1951, p. 273).

The wonderful life-changing message of the Bible is an established fact. The question is, "Has it changed your life?"

Summary and Conclusion

The Bible is the most wonderful book ever written, as uniquely demonstrated in the aforementioned ten areas.

1. Intelligent Faith:

The Bible is not merely a history book to be studied for its teachings or admired for its wisdom. In the twentieth century educated men and women still can investigate the Bible in detail and believe in its message without compromising their intellectual integrity.

2. Harmony:

Though the Bible contains 66 books written over a period of 1500 years by 40 different authors from different educational backgrounds, in different languages, on different continents, concerning many different subjects, it remains a unity—one unfolding story from beginning to end. The ultimate author behind the books of the Bible is God the Holy Spirit.

3. Survival:

The Bible has survived, intact, throughout history. The text of the Bible has been transmitted in an accurate manner so that we can be certain that it reads the same today as when originally written.

4. Historical Precision:

Although composed from 2000 to 4000 years ago, the Bible demonstrates itself to be historically accurate as to the people, places, and events it records.

5. Scientific Respectability:

When dealing with areas pertaining to science, the Bible is accurate and restrained. This is in direct contrast to other ancient works which have fanciful ideas about the nature of the universe. A correct interpretation of the facts of science and the teaching of Scripture will find that the two are not in conflict.

6. Ability To Predict The Future:

Contained within the pages of Scripture are hundreds of fulfilled prophecies. No other book, ancient or modern, has anything like this. Predictive prophecy demonstrates that God exists and that He is controlling history.

7. Honesty:

The Scriptures deal honestly with the sins of its characters. There is no attempt to whitewash their faults. This also is in contrast to most other ancient works which attempt to place their characters in the best possible light. However the main character of the Bible, Jesus Christ, is shown to be without sin, as was testified by his enemies as well as His friends.

8. Unique Teachings:

The teachings of Scripture are unique. They have not been influenced by the pagan and superstitious beliefs of the nations around them. These unique teachings include the belief in one God, the worth of man, and a genuine hope for life beyond the grave.

9. Main Character—Jesus Christ:

Jesus, the main character of Scripture, is different from any religious leader who ever has lived. An investigation of His life and deeds will show Him to be whom He claimed—the Son of God.

10. Life-Changing Message:

For the last two thousand years, the message of the Bible has been transforming lives like no other book. The message of God's love and forgiveness through Jesus Christ still is changing lives today.

The claims of a book with the remarkable credentials of the Bible deserve serious consideration. Any sincere seeker after truth should look into this book for answers to the ultimate questions of life.

The authority of Jesus Christ

When it comes to determining whether or not the Bible is the inspired word of God, we can rest confidently on the authority of Jesus Christ. We arrive at this conclusion by the following logical steps:

1. Already we have shown that the New Testament can be trusted as an accurate historical document, giving firsthand information on the life of Jesus Christ.

2. In this accurate, historical document Jesus Christ is presented as having made certain claims about Himself. He claimed to be the Messiah, the Son of God, the Way, the Truth, and the Life, the only way by which anyone can approach God.

3. Jesus Christ demonstrated that He had the right to make those claims by fulfilling prophecies about the Messiah. He performed miracles, showing He had power over nature. The most significant miracle of all was His rising from the dead (John 2:19-21). The resurrection confirmed His claim to Deity.

4. Since Jesus is the Messiah, God in human flesh, He is the last word on all matters. He had the divine authority to endorse all Scripture or only some of it. He universally affirmed all Scripture, in every part, as the Divine Word of God. Therefore we conclude the Bible, both the Old and New Testament, is the Word of God.

Have You Trusted Him?

God has given us sufficient evidence to believe. Jesus Christ is waiting for you to make a decision for Him. If you would like to become a Christian right now, pray a simple prayer like this:

Lord Jesus, I know that I'm a sinner. Thank you for dying for me. Right this moment, in the best way that I know how, I trust You as my own Savior and Lord. Thank you Lord, for saving me. In Jesus' Name, Amen.

If you just prayed this prayer, congratulations! You have decided for Jesus Christ and for eternal life.

In doing so you have established this day as your spiritual birthday, and I would like to know about it. Please take a moment to write me at: Box 6486, Orange, California, 92613. God Bless You!

About the Author

Don Stewart is one of the most successful writers in the country having authored or co-authored over twenty books. These include the award winning *Family Handbook of Christian Knowledge: The Bible, You Be The Judge,* and *The Ten Wonders of the Bible.*

Don's writings have also achieved international success. He has twenty-one books that have been translated into different languages including Chinese, Finnish, Polish, Spanish, German, and Portuguese.

Don received his undergraduate degree at Biola University majoring in Bible. He received a masters degree from Talbot Theological Seminary graduating with the highest honors. Don is a member of the national honor society, Kappa Tau Epsilon.

Don is also an internationally known apologist, a defender of the historic Christian faith. In his defense of Christianity he has traveled to over thirty countries speaking at colleges, universities, churches, seminars, and retreats. His topics include the evidence for Christianity, the identity of Jesus Christ, the challenge of the cults, and the relationship of the Bible and science. His audiences have numbered over a million people.

Because of his international success as an author and speaker, Don's various books have generated sales of over one million copies.

If you would like Don Stewart to speak at your church, retreat, seminar or school you may contact him through Dart Press, Box 6486, Orange, California, 92613. 714-754-7120.

Need More Copies?

If you cannot find this book at your local bookstore
you may order additional copies from:

Dart Press, Box 6486,
Orange, California 92613
714-754-7120

Cost is $6.95 plus $1.50 for shipping and handling.
(California residents adds 6.25% .43¢ per book sales
tax)

Discounts are available for large orders

Other Books By Don Stewart

You Be The Judge   ISBN 1-877825-02-6 $3.95

What Everybody Needs To Know About The Bible And
Science   ISBN 1-877825-04-2 $7.95

What Everybody Needs To Know About Jesus
 ISBN 1-877825-05-0 $7.95 (available Spring 1991)

What Everybody Needs To Know About God
 ISBN 1-877825-06-9 $7.95 (available Spring 1991)

All these books may be ordered from **Dart Press.** For a
complete list of books by Don Stewart please write or
call **Dart Press.**

Ann Tompert

Nothing Sticks Like a Shadow

Illustrated by Lynn Munsinger

Houghton Mifflin Company Boston

Library of Congress Cataloging in Publication Data

Tompert, Ann.
   Nothing sticks like a shadow.

   Summary: To win a bet, Rabbit tries to get rid of his shadow,
with the aid of many animal friends.
   [1. Shadows — Fiction. 2. Animals — Fiction]
I. Munsinger, Lynn, ill. II. Title.
PZ7.T598No 1984   [E]   83-18554

Printed in the United States of America

RNF   ISBN   0-395-35391-2
PAP   ISBN   0-395-47950-9

RNF BP & PAP **UNI** 10 9 8 7 6

Nothing Sticks
Like a Shadow

One day Rabbit was dancing a wild fandango in a field filled with clover. Woodchuck was watching him from the doorway of his burrow.

"Isn't it lonely, playing by yourself?" Woodchuck asked.

"I'm not alone," said Rabbit, pointing. "See my shadow? It goes where I go and does what I do."

"I know what you mean," said Woodchuck. "I can't escape my shadow either, no matter how hard I try."

"I can if I want to," said Rabbit.

"Oh, no, you can't," said Woodchuck. "No one can."

"I can too," said Rabbit.

"Can't," said Woodchuck.

And they pitched "cans" and "can'ts" at each other until Woodchuck said, "I'll bet you my hat you can't."

"Looks as if I'm going to have a new hat," said Rabbit. He ran and hid behind the trunk of a huge tree.

When he looked around, however, he found his shadow
standing beside him.

Woodchuck laughed. "You'll have to do better than that,"
he said.

Rabbit hurried over to a bunch of bushes and hid behind them. He looked around. No shadow did he see. "I've lost it!" he cried, peeking from behind the bushes at Woodchuck. "Give me your hat."

"Oh, no, you haven't," said Woodchuck, pointing.

Rabbit looked to where Woodchuck was pointing and saw his shadow's head peeking from behind the bushes, too.

"Take my advice," said Woodchuck. "Give it up. Stop wasting time. Nothing sticks like a shadow."

With this, he went into his burrow.

"Woodchuck thinks he knows everything," Rabbit said to his shadow. "But I'll show him. I'll run away from you."

And with a great leap, he set out across the field of clover.

Rabbit took longer and longer leaps. His shadow took longer and longer leaps as it followed right behind him.

Soon Rabbit came to a path beside a river. There he met
Beaver carrying a broom over his shoulder.

"Why are you running?" asked Beaver.

"I'm trying to get away from my shadow," said Rabbit.
"Woodchuck bet me his hat that I couldn't."

"Well," said Beaver, "it's easy to see you can't run away from it. See if you can sweep it away. Nothing sweeps better than a new broom, you know, and I just bought this one at the market."

"Thank you," said Rabbit.

And he began to sweep the path where his shadow lay.

Back and forth, back and forth, Rabbit swished the broom. Great whirlwinds of dust filled the air. Soon Rabbit was coated with dust. Dust got into his eyes, making them itch. Dust got into his nose. He sneezed, and then he sneezed again. But he didn't stop sweeping until he could see his shadow no longer.

"I've lost it!" he cried. "I've lost it!"

Dropping his broom, Rabbit danced a little jig. As he danced, the dust settled to the ground. And there was his shadow dancing beside him.

"I guess shadows can't be swept away," said Beaver. "I'm sorry I couldn't help you." He picked up his broom and went on his way.

No sooner had Beaver left than Skunk came along.

"Goodness!" he exclaimed. "What happened? I've never seen anyone so dirty."

"I was trying to sweep my shadow away," said Rabbit.

"Everyone knows you can't sweep away shadows," said Skunk.

"You can't hide from them or run away from them either," said Rabbit.

17

"Right," said Skunk. "When two things are stuck together, you must pull them apart."

He leaned over, grabbed Rabbit and pulled.

Nothing happened. He grabbed Rabbit again and jerked
so hard that he tumbled over backward.

Skunk was ready to try a third time when along came Fox on her way to a meeting of her Sewing Circle. "What in the world is going on?" she asked.

"I'm trying to pull Rabbit away from his shadow," said Skunk.

"Woodchuck bet me his hat that I can't get away from it," said Rabbit.

Fox looked at the shadow carefully. Then she took her scissors from her sewing basket. "Some things are too hard to tear apart," she said. "Let me see if I can cut Rabbit's shadow loose."

Clip, clip, clip, Fox went with her scissors. *Clip, clip, clip.*
Nothing happened.

Fox was still clipping when Raccoon came along.

"Well, well," Raccoon said. "What do we have here?"

"I'm trying to get rid of my shadow," Rabbit said.

"Why?" asked Raccoon. "Shadows are handy things to have. Sometimes they show you where you are going, and sometimes they show you where you've been."

"I know," said Rabbit. "But Woodchuck bet me his hat that I can't get rid of mine even if I want to."

"Did you try hiding from it?" asked Raccoon.

"Yes," said Rabbit. "But it didn't work. And I couldn't run away from it or sweep it away."

"I couldn't cut it off," said Fox.

"Let's try soaking it off," said Raccoon. And he ushered Rabbit to the river's edge.

Rabbit put one foot into the water, then jerked it out.

"It's cold!" he wailed.

"Go on," urged Raccoon.

Rabbit took a step.

"Keep going," said Raccoon.

Rabbit shivered. "It's too cold!" he cried.

He swung around to leave the river, bumped into Raccoon, and fell into the water with a great splash. The river swirled around him. He tossed and rolled, trying to get back to his feet.

Raccoon grabbed him and dragged him to shore. Rabbit was wet to the skin. Water dripped from his ears. His clothes hung on him like wet rags. Never had he felt so miserable. But the water had not washed away his shadow. There it was beside him.

"Looks as if you're stuck with your shadow," said Raccoon.

"Why don't you give up?" asked Fox.
"Tell Woodchuck he's right," said Skunk.
"I don't want to," said Rabbit. "But I guess I'll have to."
Rabbit walked slowly across the fields.

When he reached Woodchuck's burrow, Woodchuck was not at home. Rabbit stretched out on a flat sunny rock to wait for him. His shadow stretched out beside him. He was tired. The hot sun felt good. Soon steam rose from his drying clothes. He thought about moving to a shady spot, but he was too sleepy to do so.

"Anyway," he said with a yawn, "if I stay here, maybe the sun will melt my shadow away."

Rabbit tried hard to keep his eyes open to watch the sun melt his shadow. But his eyelids grew heavier and heavier until he fell asleep.

It was dark when Woodchuck shook Rabbit awake. "You win," said Woodchuck.

Rabbit yawned and stretched and rubbed the sleep from his eyes.

Woodchuck put his hat on Rabbit's head. "Congratulations," he said. "Your shadow is gone."

Rabbit turned round and round. "Oh, dear," he wailed. "The sun *did* melt my shadow."

"That's what you wanted, isn't it?" asked Woodchuck.

"No," wailed Rabbit. "I was only trying to show you that I could get rid of it if I wanted to. And now it's gone! What am I going to do without it?"

At that moment, the clouds parted. A full moon shone. And there was Rabbit's shadow.

"Look!" cried Rabbit. "It's back! You were right after all."

And he and his shadow whirled and twirled in a wild fandango.

"Of course I'm right," crowed Woodchuck, snatching his hat from Rabbit's head. "I told you that nothing sticks like a shadow."